FUNCTIONS
AND
SPREADSHEETS

GETTING DOWN TO BUSINESS

TEACHER'S GUIDE

MathScape™
SEEING AND THINKING
MATHEMATICALLY

When Creative Publications was aware of a trademark claim, the designations have been printed in initial capital letters (e.g., Coca-Cola).

Creative Publications and MathScape are trademarks or registered trademarks of Creative Publications.

© 1998 Creative Publications
1300 Villa Street
Mountain View
California 94041

Printed in the United States of America.

0-7622-0226-2
2 3 4 5 6 7 8 9 10.02 01 00 99 98

Creative Publications

Education Development Center, Inc.

Curriculum Developers for
Getting Down to Business
Kristen Herbert, Susan Janssen

EDC Project Director
Glenn M. Kleiman

EDC Core Staff
Amy Brodesky, Rebecca Brown, Dan Brutlag, Kristen Herbert, Susan Janssen, Shelley Isaacson, Andrea Tench, Dan Tobin, Karen Zweig

Other EDC Contributors
Al Cuoco, E. Paul Goldenberg, Marlene Kliman, Leigh Peake, Sue Rasala, Faye Ruopp, Kimberly Smart, Ellen Smith, Marianne Thompson, Albertha Walley, Muffie Wiebe

Additional Contributors
Grace Benigno, Frank Cabesaz, Amy Doherty, Mary Lou Mehrling, Fran Ostrander, Stacie Cassat

Project Collaborators & Consultants
EdMath, Victoria, Australia:
Charles Lovitt, Doug Clarke, Ian Lowe

Shell Centre for Mathematical Education, University of Nottingham, England: Hugh Burkhardt, Rosemary Caddy, Malcolm Swan

Inverness Research Associates, Inverness, CA: Barbara Heenan, Mark St. John

Brookline Public Schools, Brookline, MA: Robert Bates

ACKNOWLEDGMENTS

 MathScape Background

The STM project built upon EDC's 40-year history of developing educational materials, including PSSC Physics, ESS Science, The Infinity Factory television series, Insights Science, The Geometric Supposer software series, My Travels with Gulliver, and many other curriculum, software, and video products.

This unit is one of a series of twenty-one MathScape: Seeing and Thinking Mathematically units designed to fully address current standards and recommendations for teaching middle school mathematics. The Seeing and Thinking Mathematically project involved international collaboration with:

- The Shell Centre for Mathematical Education at the University of Nottingham, England, whose contributions built upon many years of research and development underlying materials such as The Language of Functions and Graphs.

- EdMath of Victoria, Australia, whose staff built upon years of research and development producing materials such as the Mathematics Curriculum and Teaching Program (MCTP) materials.

- Inverness Research Associates of California provided consulting on the design of the research processes used in the project and conducted research for several of the units.

The Seeing and Thinking Mathematically project incorporated many formative research activities to assist the developers in designing materials that are mathematically clear and pedagogically effective with diverse populations of students. These activities included summer institutes with middle school teachers, consultations with experts on teaching mathematics to students from different cultural and linguistic backgrounds, reviews of the research on children's learning of mathematics, input from many consultants and advisors, and classroom testing of activities in which the project staff and teachers worked closely together. These research activities helped to define the design principles used throughout the curriculum.

Building from the design principles, initial versions of each unit were then carefully tested in a variety of classrooms, insuring feedback from multiple teachers and diverse groups of students. Project researchers conducted weekly classroom observations and teacher interviews. Student work was collected and analyzed to evaluate the lessons and identify common student misconceptions. The project researchers and curriculum developers used this extensive field test data to revise and improve the units. The field test teachers' classroom experiences and suggestions were also incorporated into the final units in the form of "From the Classroom" notes and "A Teacher Reflects."

This unit of MathScape: Seeing and Thinking Mathematically was developed by the Seeing and Thinking Mathematically project (STM), based at Education Development Center, Inc. (EDC), a nonprofit educational research and development organization in Newton, MA. The STM project was supported, in part, by the National Science Foundation Grant No. 9054677. Opinions expressed are those of the authors and not necessarily those of the Foundation.

Field Test Teachers

We wish to extend special thanks to the following teachers and their students for their roles in field testing and reviewing units developed by EDC.

ARLINGTON, MA
Carol Martignette
  Boswell
Steve Porretta

BELMONT, MA
Tony Guarante
Heidi Johnson

BOSTON, MA
Patricia Jorsling
George Perry
Elizabeth Prieto
Bill Rudder

BROOKLINE, MA
Robert Bates
Frank Cabezas
Carolyn Connolly
Arlene Geller-Petrini
Sandra Hegsted
Oakley Hoerth
Judy McCarthy
Carol Mellet
Fran Ostrander
Barbara Scotto
Rhonda Weinstein

Debbie Winkler
Deanna Wong

CAMBRIDGE, MA
Mary Lou Mehring
Jennie Schmidt
Jesse Solomon

FREMONT, CA
Julie Dunkle

INDIO, CA
Lisa Sullivan

LAKEVIEW, CA
Jane Fesler

MILL VALLEY, CA
Patty Armstrong

NEW CANAAN, CT
Sue Kelsey
Bruce Lemoine

NEWTON, MA
Sonya Grodberg
David Lawrence
Mark Rubel

SAN FRANCISCO, CA
Ardreina Gualco
Ingrid Oyen

SOMERVILLE, MA
Jean Foley

**SOUTH SAN
  FRANCISCO, CA**
Doug Harik

SUDBURY, MA
Fred Gross
Sondra Hamilton
Jackie Simms

TEMECULA, CA
Ray Segal

TIBURON, CA
Julie Askeland

WALTHAM, MA
Amy Doherty
Diane Krueger
Pat Maloney

We extend our appreciation to Judy Mumme and the following teachers and educators involved in the California Middle School Mathematics Renaissance Project.

Cathy Carroll
SAN MATEO, CA

Deb Clay
HUNTINGTON BEACH, CA

Kathryn Conley
MERCED, CA

Joan Easterday
SANTA ROSA, CA

Linda Fisher
SANTA CRUZ, CA

Marty Hartrick
SAN FRANCISCO, CA

Kevin Jordan
CARMEL, CA

Steve Leliever
LONG BEACH, CA

Carole Maples
WALNUT CREEK, CA

Guillermo Mendieta
AZUSA, CA

Teferi Messert
SACRAMENTO, CA

Mark Rubell
NEWTON, CA

Charles Schindler
RUNNING SPRINGS, CA

Aminah Talib
CARSON, CA

Kevin Truitt
LOS ANGELES, CA

Classroom Testing Teachers

Our thanks to the following classroom teachers for their contributions on the MathScape units.

Heidi Ackley
Steve Ackley
Penelope Jo Black
Bev Brockhoff
Geoff Borroughs
Linda Carmen
Janet Casagrande
Karen Chamberlin
Laura Chan
April Cherrington
Peggy Churchill
Marian Connelly
Jack Cox
Allen Craig
Barbara Creedon
Bill Cummins
Phyllis Cummins
Kathy Duane
Jennifer Dunmire
Karen Edmonds
Sara Effenbeck
Jodie Foster
John Friedrich
Barbara Gneiting
Lisa Gonzales
Ardreina Gualco
Doug Harik
Jennifer Hogerty
Lynn Hoggatt
Ron Johnson
Judy Jones
Sue Lackey
Joan LaComb
Stan Lake
Amanda LaRocca

Claudia Larson
Mona Lasley
Maria Majka
Jim McHugh
Fernando Mendez
Michael Merk
Carol Moore
John Mulkerrins
John Osness
Mary Ann Pella-
  Donnelly
Charles Perez
Dave Peters
Linda Peters
Lisa Phillips
Jim Pinckard
Ron Rice
Mark Ristow
Thelma Rodriguez
Ellen Ron
Emiliano Sanchez
Wes Schroeder
Janet Schwarz
Cindi Sekera
Doris Selden
Gale Sunderland
Jim Tearpak
Barbara Termaat
Brenda Walker
David Ward
Brenda Watson
Howard Web
Nancy Withers
Hanne Young

Creative Publications Staff and Contributors

Curriculum Director
Linda Charles

MathScape Product Development Team
Ema Arcellana, Katie Azevedo, Bettina Borer, Lynn Clark, Kirstin Cruikshank, Vivien Freund, Janice Gaal, Lorraine Groff, Susan Guthrie, Chris Hofer, John Kerwin, Ed Lazar, Heidi Lewis, Mary Scott Martinson, Gregg McGreevy, Andrea Moore, Judith Bao Roubideaux, Lynn Sanchez, Lyn Savage, Vickie Self, Joe Shines, Joe Todaro, Miguel Villaseñor, Linda Ward, Sandra Ward, Debra Webster, Stephanie Wooldridge

Credits
Photography: Chris Conroy • Beverley Harper (cover) • © Peter Poulides/Tony Stone Images: p. 27BC • Images ©1997 PhotoDisc, Inc.: pp. 9TR, 63B. Illustrations: Gary Taxali • Manfred Geier • Mike Reed • Burton Morris • Susan Williams • Greg Stadler: p. 3BL • Amanda Haley, pp. R2TL, R8F, R13F.

Student Guide Credits:
Photography: Chris Conroy • Beverley Harper (cover) • Images ©1997 PhotoDisc, Inc.: pp. 3R, 28. Illustrations: Amanda Haley: pp. 2, 6–7, 9–11, 23, 31, 34 • Greg Stadler: pp. 22, 26–27, 30, 38TL, 45BR.

Other Contributors: Amparo del Rio Design • © Sunburst Communications, 1998: p. 13BL • GTS Graphics, Inc. • Manufactured by Banta Book Group.

TABLE OF

Functions and Spreadsheets

In the investigations in this unit, students play the roles of business owners and consultants as they learn to use spreadsheets on the computer and graphs to explore the relationships among profit, income, and expenses.

PHASE ONE

Business Simulation

Students play and then analyze a simulation in which they assume the role of the owner of a small food booth at a school fund-raising fair. They learn to pose their suggestions for improving their food booths as what-if questions.

PHASE TWO

Spreadsheets

Students are introduced to spreadsheets and use spreadsheets to investigate several what-if questions they created in the last phase. This prepares students for writing about their top recommendations for increasing profit at their food booths.

CONTENTS

THINGS YOU SHOULD KNOW

MathScape™ is a comprehensive three-year middle school mathematics curriculum. *Getting Down to Business* Teacher's Guide contains complete lesson plans, assessment, and reproducible pages. *Getting Down to Business* Student Guide contains lesson pages and homework. MathScape is supported by a *hot* **words**™, *hot* **topics**™ handbook for students at each grade level. The handbook contains a glossary, how-to information, and problems for additional homework and practice.

 This icon identifies **notes** of special interest within the teaching steps. These notes often include an indication of what to expect from student writing or discussions. This is also where you will find classroom management tips, information on the rationale behind particular investigations, and some answers.

 This icon identifies comments that have come from teachers who have used this unit in the classroom. Their experiences and practical suggestions for working through the unit appear in the margin of the Teacher's Guide, next to the teaching steps of each lesson. These **comments from the classroom** may include descriptions of student dialogue, ideas for responding to student misconceptions, varied approaches that address diversity in the classroom, management tips, and suggestions for extending lesson activities.

student page → When appropriate, a reduced version of the **Student Guide** page is shown on the Teacher's Guide page for easy reference. The arrow icon is used to indicate which steps on the Teacher's Guide page correspond directly to the steps on the Student Guide page.

The *hot* **words** that appear on the lesson pages in the Student Guide are mathematical terms related to the lesson. The *hot* **topics** appearing in the Teacher's Guide indicate mathematical topics that are recommended for optional review and homework.

If your students have access to the *hot* **words**, *hot* **topics** handbook, they can locate the definitions of the *hot* **words** in the *hot* **words** section of the handbook. You can also direct students to the *hot* **topics** in the handbook, where they will find instruction, examples, and exercises.

If your students do not have the *hot* **words**, *hot* **topics** handbook, you can use *hot* **words** for discussion, referencing them in any mathematical glossary or dictionary. You can use the recommended *hot* **topics** as a guide to help you organize supplemental review materials.

UNIT MATERIALS

The following materials are required for the lessons in *Getting Down to Business.*

PER STUDENT

- calculator

PER GROUP

- number cubes labeled 1–6

PER CLASS

- chart paper

- 4 or more computers with spreadsheet programs such as The Cruncher, Excel, Lotus, or ClarisWorks

GETTING DOWN TO BUSINESS

FUNCTIONS AND SPREADSHEETS

a business entrepreneur ponders questions such as these: What if we could reduce our expenses? What would happen if we raised our prices? What if we added more staff? Underlying these questions is a functional relationship among the numbers that govern the business that we can express by the formula Profit = Income − Expenses *(PIE)*.

In this unit, students explore this formula, as well as the concept of functional relationships, by playing the roles of business owners and business consultants. Whether mirroring business situations or playing simulations, students learn to organize data into tables and graphs, pose what-if questions, test their ideas in spreadsheets on the computer and in simulations, and make recommendations supported by data. Throughout the unit, students are learning a process for using the PIE relationship to make informed decisions.

PHASE ONE

Business Simulation

Phase One introduces students to business concepts by discussing their own experiences with businesses and analyzing a simple business scenario to predict how that business will do. This prepares students to play a simulation in which they assume the role of the owner of a small food booth at a school fund-raising fair. Students analyze the simulation and relate the results to the Profit = Income − Expenses relationship. They then make suggestions for improving their food booths and learn to pose these suggestions as what-if questions.

PHASE TWO

Spreadsheets

Phase Two emphasizes the use of spreadsheets on the computer. After students are introduced to spreadsheets, they use them to investigate several what-if questions they created in the last lesson. Students pair up on the computer to play a game in which one student must figure out a partner's hidden spreadsheet formula. They then discuss what they learned about spreadsheet notation, and generate their own lists of tips and suggestions to each other for using the spreadsheet. Students add data to a spreadsheet on the computer and use it to explore ways to make their food booths more profitable. After they explore their own what-if questions, they write about their top recommendation for increasing profit.

Spreadsheets and Graphs

In Phase Three, students assume the role of consultants to the Tee-Time T-Shirt Company. They begin by creating a graph of price and the number of people who would buy T-shirts. They explore relationships among the points and between the two axes of the graph. Students create a spreadsheet that they use to explore the effect of price and number of sales on expenses and income, and therefore on profit. They use the results from their spreadsheet investigation to create graphs showing the relationships between price and income, price and expenses, and price and profit. Students complete their role as consultants when they use qualitative graphs to further explore the Profit = Income − Expenses relationship.

A Case Study of North Mall Cinema

In the last phase, students begin their final project, which consists of a case study that continues throughout the phase. Students organize the information for the North Mall Cinema, a business that wants to improve its profits, and work in groups to generate a list of possible what-if questions to pose. They build a spreadsheet from scratch on the computer and use it to explore the what-if questions they generated previously. They end the phase by writing a report to North Mall with their recommendations for improving profit. The assessment for this unit involves the work students did for this case study.

MathScape: *n:* A view of the world from a mathematical perspective.

Math Themes

Getting Down to Business incorporates the math themes of **Functional Relationships** and **Multiple Representations.** The idea that one set of numbers is related to another set of numbers is a powerful one in mathematics. Functions enable us to express and explore some real-life situations numerically, and make predictions of trends based upon the numbers.

Such a relationship implies that as one set of numbers changes, the other set of numbers also changes according to some rules of the relationship. The equation Profit = Income − Expenses *(PIE)*, for example, implies that if expenses remain constant, then as income increases, profits increase as well. If expenses increase more than income, profits decrease. Understanding a specific relationship such as this lays the groundwork for a general understanding of functions.

This unit helps students understand functions by relating three different representations: equations, graphs, and spreadsheets. Simple equations express the relationship between profit, income, and expenses; or between income, number sold, and price. Students examine functions using line graphs in which each axis represents a set of numbers, and the graph shows a picture of the relationship. As students explore different problems using the spreadsheet, they come to understand how changing one set of numbers affects other numbers.

THE MATHSCAPE

Math Processes

So much emphasis is placed on problem solving in the mathematics classroom that the equally valuable skill of problem posing is often overlooked. Yet scientists, mathematicians, and others use problem posing (making hypotheses and predictions) to frame, guide, and extend their work. In this unit, students explore ways of increasing a business's profits by posing and solving their own what-if questions.

These what-if questions vary one or more elements of the Profit = Income − Expenses relationship. For example, a student wants to investigate the problem, "How could you double the profit for your food booth?" The student can then pose questions that vary different mathematical elements of the relationship, such as "What if I charged higher prices?" or "What if I spent less on my supplies?" As they vary certain elements and see the results, students deepen their understanding of functional relationships in general and, more specifically, how income and expenses interact to determine profits.

When using a spreadsheet, students can change one element of the mathematical relationship and the computer performs the repetitive calculations almost instantly. This enables students to explore more what-if variations and deepen their understanding of the functional relationship.

Math Strands

In this unit, students' work focuses on the strands of Number/Operations and Algebra/Functions.

Throughout the unit, students use calculations to solve problems within the business context. This gives meaning to the calculations and results; a negative result is not simply a negative number, it might mean that your business is losing money! Students also explore functions in the same meaningful context: discovering how changing I and E affects P in the equation $P = I − E$ makes good sense when talking about profit, income, and expenses.

Many of the problem situations involve repeatedly varying elements of a relationship; and searching for ways to reduce expenses, increase income, and thereby maximize profits. This leads to using spreadsheets, the powerful computer tool designed for exactly this type of situation.

Spreadsheets help students understand the purpose and use of formulas. As students create their own spreadsheets in Lessons 6, 8, and 11, they express these relationships as formulas written in spreadsheet notation and begin to understand how a formula allows them to express a relationship generally.

Students also explore these functional relationships graphically, using both sketched graphs without numbers to show general patterns, and more exact graphs to show exact numerical relationships.

NCTM CURRICULUM STANDARDS FOR GRADES 5–8

The standards that correlate to the content in this unit are checked.

✔ Mathematics as Problem Solving

✔ Mathematics as Communication

✔ Mathematics as Reasoning

✔ Mathematical Connections

   Number and Number Relationships

   Number Systems and Number Theory

✔ Computation and Estimation

✔ Patterns and Functions

   Algebra

✔ Statistics

   Probability

   Geometry

✔ Measurement

PREREQUISITES

The investigations in *Getting Down to Business* will be most successful if students enter the unit with some experience in the following skills:

- ability to organize data into tables

- knowledge of basic skills necessary to use a calculator

- understanding of what formulas are and how to write equations

- familiarity with creating and reading line graphs

If your students need preliminary work with these skills, you may want to review:

hot words

- formula
- equation

hot topics

- Displaying Data
- Setting Up Expressions and Equations

Have students review the unit overview on page 2–3 in the Student Guide.

The following question is posed on page 2 of the *Getting Down to Business* Student Guide: What math is used to increase profits? This question is investigated in the following pre-assessment activity, which generates class discussion. It also results in individual writing that helps reveal how much students know about organizing data, making calculations, writing formulas, and posing what-if questions to test out the profitability of a new business.

Materials

Per Student:

- calculator
- computer
- spreadsheet software

Prerequisite Check

As students discuss different ways to make a profit in a business, ask them to brainstorm ideas about what they would need to set up a class bake sale. If they need help getting started, you might suggest renting space, paying employees, and finding out the price of flour, napkins, and other materials. Then students could work in groups or individually to set up a table with these column headings: item, cost, price. Have each group estimate the cost of each item on its chart.

If students use the words *price* and *cost* incorrectly, do not be concerned. This concept will be covered in Phase One, and students will continue to be exposed to business terms throughout the unit.

Performance Task

The following activity can be done individually or in pairs. Explain to students that they will be learning about and using spreadsheets in this unit. Let them know that they will be solving problems similar to this in the unit. Students should be able to complete this activity by choosing one of these tools: mental math, paper and pencil, calculator, or spreadsheet.

- Come up with a plan to make a profit of $100 at the class bake sale.

- Choose one of the following tools and explain how you would use it to figure out your profit: mental math, paper and pencil, calculator, or spreadsheet.

Ask students to write in response to the question: What math is used to increase profits?

In the Assessment pages that accompany this unit, see Pre-assessment page A4 for assessment information and sample student work.

PLANNING AND PACING

A Typical Path Through the Unit

This unit takes approximately 25 class periods, each lasting 45 minutes. You can use a copy of the Assessment Checklist, Reproducible page R1, as a planning tool to record the days you will spend on each lesson. Here are some things you will want to keep in mind as you plan for this unit.

- A typical lesson takes about two days. The amount of time you spend on a lesson may be influenced by the demands of your particular class.

- The amount of time you spend on the final project depends on how much work students do outside of class.

I had the class complete the first three phases where they explored the PIE function in a variety of ways—through a simulation, spreadsheets, and graphs. I felt that my students had learned to use all these tools, pose questions, and make recommendations from data.
Phase One: Remains as is.
Phase Two: Remains as is.
Phase Three: Remains as is.
Phase Four: Cut this phase.
Time: 18 class sessions ☐

My students had lots of prior experience with graphs, so I spent more time focusing on spreadsheets. My students did the simulation in the first phase, began exploring the PIE relationship, and learned to pose what-if questions. In the second phase, they learned to use a spreadsheet. I found that I needed to give students more support in creating their spreadsheets from scratch in the last phase.
Phase One: Remains as is.
Phase Two: Remains as is.
Phase Three: Cut this phase.
Phase Four: Remains as is.
Time: 18 class sessions ☐

Getting Down to Business ASSESSMENT CHECKLIST

Name:	Assignment Description	Assessment	Notes
Lesson			Day 1
Pre-assessment	What math is used to increase profits?		Days 2-3
Lesson 1	To Sell or Not to Sell Gourmet Hot Dogs		Days 4-5
Lesson 2	A Food Booth at a School Fair		Days 6-7
Lesson 3	What-If Questions for the Food Booth		
Phase One Skill Check	Skill Quiz 1 & Homework 1–3		Days 8-9
Lesson 4	What-If Questions on Spreadsheets		Days 10-11
Lesson 5	"What's My Formula?" Game		Days 12-13
Lesson 6	Double Your Profits?		
Phase Two Skill Check	Skill Quiz 2 & Homework 4–6		Days 14-15
Lesson 7	How Many Sales at Tee-Time?		Days 16-17
Lesson 8	How Much Profit at Tee-Time?		Days 18-19
Lesson 9	Months Later at Tee-Time		
Phase Three Skill Check	Skill Quiz 3 & Homework 7–9		Days 20-21
Lesson 10	North Mall Cinema's Project		Days 22-23
Lesson 11	North Mall Cinema's Spreadsheet		Days 24-25
Lesson 12	North Mall Cinema's Report		
Phase Four Skill Check	Skill Quiz 4 & Homework 10–12		
Post-assessment	What math is used to increase profits?		

Period: Date:

Comments:

CURRICULUM LINKS

This unit can be part of an interdisciplinary unit on entrepreneurship, or it can connect to Social Studies by focusing on the economics of a historical period or place. The following books and materials provide good starting points for students to observe the link between mathematics and other subjects.

The Toothpaste Millionaire

By Jean Merrill

Good reading about how friends made $1 million by creating and marketing a cheaper and better toothpaste. Also recommended are *Eddie Incorporated* by Phyllis Naylor, and *Rusty Timmons' First Million* by Joan Davenport Carris.

Biz Kids Guide to Success

By Teri Thompson

This short, easy-to-read guide takes students through the steps involved in starting their own business. A more detailed guide is *A Teen's Guide to Business* by Linda Menzies.

The New Youth Entrepreneur

By Marilyn Kourilsky

This 12-module unit shows students how to start their own businesses. It is available on microfiche through ERIC (ED 393529-ED393541) or contact the Center for Entrepreneurial Leadership (816) 932-1000.

"From Riot to Ruin, a Surprising Harvest"

By Larry Armstrong

The May 9, 1994, issue of *Business Week* tells the story of how Food from the Hood marketed salad dressing. Back issues of this magazine make a good classroom resource.

The Cruncher®

By Davidson & Associates, Inc.

The Cruncher® is a spreadsheet program that is kid-friendly and fun to use. It is also powerful enough to meet the needs of most spreadsheet users. It is available for Macintosh or Windows. Call (800) 545-7677 for more information.

Other Resources

Junior Achievement provides business consultants to teach economics in your classroom. For information on this free program, call (719) 540-8000 or connect to one of their Yahoo web sites.

KEY WORDS

The following words will serve as starting points for students who want to further explore the concepts presented in this unit.

- **entrepreneur**
- **youth business**
- **money-making**
- **budget**
- **economics— juvenile literature**

Business Simulation

Assuming the role of owner of a
food booth, students play and
analyze a business simulation in
terms of profit, income, and
expenses.

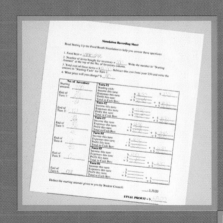

AT A GLANCE

To Sell or Not to Sell Gourmet Hot Dogs

Students talk about their own business experiences before they read and analyze a simple business scenario about a food booth. As they discuss the scenario and predict how successful the business might be, students begin to think about how income and expenses interact to determine profit. Thinking about the mathematical relationships among income, expenses, and profit begins the process of discovering ways to increase profits using functions and spreadsheets.

Mathematical Goals

- Explore the concepts of income, expenses, and profit.

- Begin to explore the relationships among income, expenses, and profit.

- Make recommendations based on data.

MATERIALS

PER STUDENT

- Reproducible R8

PER CLASS

- chart paper

A Food Booth at a School Fair

Students play a simulation where they take on the role of the owner of a food booth at a school fund-raising fair. They first play the simulation with the class and then in pairs, keeping track of information as they make decisions about how to run their booths. This simulation introduces the calculation of income, expenses, and profit, and the meaning of a mathematical relationship. As students play the simulation, they gain an intuitive sense of this relationship before establishing a written equation for it.

Mathematical Goals

- Understand how changes in income and expenses can affect profit.

- Calculate income, expenses, and profit.

- Record information in a table.

MATERIALS

PER STUDENT

- calculator (optional)

- Reproducibles R9, R11, and R12

- Reproducible R10 (2 copies)

PER PAIR

- 2 number cubes labeled 1–6

PREPARATION

Read page 12. Students need the Simulation Recording Sheets from the second time they play the simulation for Lessons 3 and 6. Students will work with the same partners in Lesson 6.

LESSON 3

What-If Questions for the Food Booth

What if we had charged a different price at our food booth? Students explore this question to help them analyze their simulations. They think about changes they would make in running their food booths by testing how profits change at various prices and predicting the effects on income and expenses. Students organize data, pose what-if questions, investigate the results of those questions, and make recommendations based on the results. The lesson ends with a phase assessment of students' understanding of profit, income, and expenses.

MATERIALS

PER STUDENT

• Reproducible R13

PREPARATION

Students will need the Simulation Recording Sheets from the second time they played the simulation in Lesson 2. Be sure they save these for Lesson 6.

Mathematical Goals

- Pose what-if questions.

- Describe, in general terms, the algorithm for calculating profit.

- Calculate income by multiplying number sold by price.

MATH BACKGROUND

Purpose of the Simulation in Lesson 2

This simulation provides concrete experiences from the role of a business owner. Students can draw upon this information throughout the unit and achieve a better sense of the following:

- the $P = I - E$ relationship, which students first describe in words and then formalize into an equation by the end of the simulation

- the algorithm for calculating income:
  Income = Number sold × Price

- the difference between income and profit

- simple examples of the relationships among expenses, income, and profit

- the decisions a business owner makes

How the Simulation Works in Lesson 2

1. When students play in pairs, they each get a copy of the Simulation Recording Sheet (Reproducible page R10).

2. Before starting, each pair makes the initial decisions from Setting Up the Food Booth Simulation (Reproducible page R9):

- What food item to sell? It makes no difference which item students choose.

- How many items to purchase for inventory? Each pair starts with $50 to buy inventory once at the beginning of the game, and sells from

that inventory throughout the game. Students keep a running total of remaining inventory items on the Simulation Recording Sheet.

- What price to charge per item? Each pair chooses a price to use throughout the game. Students see the effect of charging a price, and compare results with classmates who charged different prices.

3. Students read the Simulation Rules (Student Guide page 8). To begin a turn, they roll the number cubes to select an Income transaction from Income Results, Reproducible page R11, and record information on the Simulation Recording Sheet. They repeat this process with the Expense Results, Reproducible page R12. If there are no expenses, students record $0 to reinforce the $P = I - E$ algorithm.

Students calculate profit by subtracting the expenses (if any) from the income generated during this turn.

4. Students keep track of inventory sold in the Inventory column on the Simulation Recording Sheet.

5. The game lasts six turns, or until students run out of inventory. If students need to sell more items than they have, they sell the remainder of their inventory, record the income, and roll for expenses to finish the turn. Then they calculate their final profit.

TECHNOLOGY OPTIONS

Four-Function Calculators

Students are expected to have access to four-function calculators and will save time when they use calculators to compute inventory, expenses, income, and profit during the business simulation in Lesson 2. Students will benefit from access to calculators in Lesson 3 when they explore the question: What if I charge a different price?

Simulation Software

The simulation in Lesson 2 provides students with initial experience in running a business. To further develop their understanding of profit, income, and expenses, students can explore electronic simulations of businesses, such as Hot Dog Stand: The Works®, by Sunburst. As students play the simulation game, they make decisions about the quantity of inventory to purchase, and prices to charge. They also consider variables that impact sales at a concession stand.

Spreadsheets in the Unit

In the next phase, students will begin working with spreadsheets. The spreadsheet's ability to recalculate data as different information is entered makes it the ideal tool for exploring the relationship between different sets of data. The unit focuses on teaching students how to use a spreadsheet to investigate certain mathematical relationships including: 1) understanding how a spreadsheet works, and how it can be used; 2) entering text, numbers, and simple formulas in a spreadsheet, keeping in mind that spreadsheets follow a standard order of operations; 3) creating a simple spreadsheet to investigate a particular problem. The unit is not intended to teach students all they might need to know about spreadsheets.

Analyzing a Simple Business Scenario

Here are some of the responses I got when I wrote profit, income, cost, *and* expenses *on chart paper:*

• Profit: *the amount of money you make or earn*

• Loss: *losing money or something*

• Cost: *the price of your product*

• Expenses: *like you have to pay for electricity. It's everything you need. Materials, I guess.*

I was struck by how students could give generic definitions for all the terms except expenses, *for which they had to give concrete examples.* □

To Sell or Not to Sell Gourmet Hot Dogs

Have students review the phase overview on pages 4–5 in the Student Guide.

1 Discussing Business Experiences

Let students know that at the beginning of this unit they will be playing the role of a business owner, and later on they will become business consultants. Because many students have had business experiences as customers, pose these questions to encourage them to think about experiences they've had related to owning a business.

▪ What businesses have you or your family worked in?

▪ Have you ever run a business? What did you do?

▪ What do you think a business is?

▪ What kinds of decisions do business owners make? What parts of the business can they control?

On chart paper, list these terms: profit, income, cost, and expenses. Ask students what they think these terms mean, and write their comments. Leave the chart on display so that the class can revise these definitions and add more terms as they progress through the unit.

Initially, although students may use the appropriate language of business, they may not understand the concepts. As they gain understanding, students may use words that do not correspond to the correct business term, even though they now understand the concepts. For example, students may use *price* and *cost* interchangeably, even though they understand the difference between the amount charged to a customer *(price)* and the amount a business pays to acquire inventory *(cost)*. Listen carefully to their use of business terms and bring out different ways of describing the concepts.

student page

2 Reading the Hot Dog Stand Script

Have a few students act out the script on Reproducible R8, The Hot Dog Stand (Part 1), or read it aloud in small groups. This script helps to introduce the simulation in the next lesson. You might want students to take notes about what they think is important in the script.

Students may be unfamiliar with how some businesses make a profit—that businesses first purchase inventory at a low cost, then raise the price and sell it to their customers. You may want to point out the process that the students in the script are following in order to make a profit for their small business. Your explanation will help prepare students for the simulation in the next lesson.

Student work shown on the following pages is provided as a guide only and is not intended as an answer key.

Getting Down to Business
Student Guide page 36
Solutions: Assessment page A29

hot topics

- *Using and Finding Percents*
- *Analyzing Data*

PROFIT	INCOME	COST	EXPENS...
how much you make without being in debt	how much money you get in a long period of time	the money that stuff you sell is worth	when you need to... things for your company – they are expenses
...oney you ...ke off of ...at you're ...ing	when you go to work and bring home money	how much the items you are going to sell cost	the money you're going to spend on things you're going to sell... office supplies
...y you ...after ...ay	like your paycheck	the price of an item	the money you have to take out to pay taxes
...ne-...ra ...rice	something you live off of	how much you have to pay people who work for you	the money you owe for something

---

1 To Sell or Not to Sell Gourmet Hot Dogs

ANALYZING A SIMPLE BUSINESS SCENARIO

Imagine what it would be like to run your own business. Businesses are always looking for ways to improve their profit. You will learn about the business terms *profit, income,* and *expenses* as you analyze this example of a food booth run by students.

Read the Hot Dog Stand Script

What are the meanings of profit, income, and expenses?

Read the information in the box The Hot Dog Stand Introduction. Then think about the meanings of profit, income, and expenses in business terms as you read the script on the handout The Hot Dog Stand Part 1.

The Hot Dog Stand Introduction

Scene: It is 8:00 AM at your favorite Middle School. Three students are setting up their hot dog stand as one of the food booths at the school fund-raising fair.

Cast: Student 1 is eager to run a hot dog stand, but wants it to be out of the ordinary. Student 2 agrees with Student 1. Student 3 wants to have a regular hot dog stand because people will be familiar with it.

GETTING DOWN TO BUSINESS   LESSON 1
6   © Creative Publications • MathScape

Some of my students didn't remember the important ideas from The Hot Dog Stand (Part 1) script, so I suggested that they review the script and refer to it as they wrote their suggestions. I felt that this helped them keep the ideas fresh in their minds and resulted in suggestions that were more relevant to improving the business. □

I took the time to allow students to share their suggestions with the class. I think this was a valuable learning experience because classmates asked each other questions about ways of improving the business, which eased the transition into the next lesson. □

3 Analyzing the Hot Dog Stand Business

Ask students to work in small groups to share their ideas about whether or not the hot dog stand will be successful. Then bring the class together to discuss the basic business concepts.

The purpose of this investigation is to help students articulate their own understanding of the relationships among profit, income, and expenses. As groups of students work, circulate among them, offering assistance as needed. If they need help getting started, encourage them to look at the choices students faced in the script and the decisions they made. These include choosing to sell hot dogs, what to spend start-up money on, whether to borrow money to cover all expenses, and what price to charge.

4 Improving the Hot Dog Stand

After students have written their letters with suggestions for improving the business, encourage them to share their opinions with the class. Questions such as these will help students modify or expand the definitions of terms from Step 1:

- Did the meaning of profit, income, cost, or expenses change for you? How?

- What is something new you learned in this lesson that made you think about them differently?

Emphasize to students the importance of basing their recommendations on data provided in the script, rather than on their own personal preferences or intuitions. Basing recommendations on data is a skill that students will build throughout the unit.

DO STUDENTS' LETTERS INCLUDE:

- *legitimate business decisions related to the hot dog stand?*
- *a valid reason for agreeing or disagreeing with each decision?*

See *Getting Down to Business* Assessment page A5 for assessment information.

1. Yes, I think the hot dog stand will make a profit because I think some people will buy gourmet hot dogs with good toppings.

2. The business gets in the money ... the hot ... from ...

Improving The Hot Dog Stand.

or Students!
The decisions the ... mpoyees made were to decide ... sell gourmet hot dogs, put ... also on hot dogs. I disagree with each decision the employees made because hardly anybody would pay $1.25 or $2.00 for a hot dog. They need to charge about $1.50 for their hot dogs so that they can ... more boisness. If you are ... urmet hot dog put

---

Analyze the Hot Dog Stand Business

Talk with the members of your group about the Hot Dog Stand. Consider these questions in your investigation.

1 Do you think the Hot Dog Stand will make any profit? Why or why not?

2 Where will this business get its income? What are this business's expenses? Show your thinking.

3 What would you do differently if you were running the business?

4 Is there a chance they could lose money? How could that happen?

Improve the Hot Dog Stand

Write a letter to the students who are running the Hot Dog Stand, describing your suggestions for improving their business. Think about the decisions the students made when setting up the Hot Dog Stand. Include answers to these questions in your suggestions.

- What are the decisions the students made about setting up their business?

- Do you agree or disagree with each decision the students made? Why?

> **What do you know about profit, income, and expenses, and how they are related?**

hot words | income expense

Homework
page 36

Running a Food Booth Simulation

Students worked well in pairs to set up their simulations and to make decisions. This gave the simulation an air of reality. Students liked the idea that they would be running an imaginary business and making decisions for themselves! Some students were having heated debates over the benefits of selling chocolate chip cookies versus potato chips! □

Most students had trouble beginning the simulation, but once they were into it they all seemed to be actually having fun! One group pointed out that another group made a huge profit of $900 because they had misplaced decimals. □

A Food Booth at a School Fair

1 Setting Up the Food Booth Simulation

Distribute the following reproducibles to students: Setting Up the Food Booth Simulation (R9), Simulation Recording Sheet (R10), Income Results (R11), and Expense Results (R12). Allow time for students to read the steps in the Setting Up the Food Booth Simulation reproducible and make the decisions involved.

This simulation is intended to give students the experience of being a business owner, making some of the same kinds of decisions a business owner would make. It is intentionally kept simple. Students sell only one kind of item so that they can focus on the mathematics of the Profit = Income − Expenses equation in its simplest form.

student page

2 Playing the Simulation with the Class

After students have read the simulation rules in the Student Guide, have the class play the simulation together as you roll the two number cubes. As the class plays, emphasize the *mathematical* relationship between profit, income, and expenses rather than the business topics. Help students focus on how the changes in income and expenses affect their profit. Although students will gain a sense of this relationship the first time

through the simulation, the relationship will be made more explicit and explored in more depth as the unit progresses.

This is the first of two times that students will play the simulation in this lesson. The first time, all students will experience the same transactions. From this common experience, the class can discuss the simulation in the next step and see the effect of different people's decisions on their final profit. In Step 4, students will play in pairs, and each pair will have different transactions.

Some students may get negative values for profit in a single turn, if their expenses exceed their income. Many students do not have a sense of what happens if they spend more than they make during the simulation, unless they have learned about negative numbers. Be prepared to help students think about a loss in terms of a net result that lowers their profit, rather than as "negative money." Most students will have a positive final profit at the end of the simulation, and may only encounter negative profit during a single turn.

LESSON HOMEWORK

Getting Down to Business
Student Guide page 37
Solutions: Assessment page A30

hot topics

- *Integer Operations*
- *Collecting Data*

Simulation Recording Sheet

Read Setting Up the Food Booth Simulation to help you answer these questions.

1. Food Item = _choc chip cookies_
2. Number of items bought for inventory = _250_. Write the number in "Starting Amount" at the top of the No. of Inventory column.
3. Total cost of these items = $ _39.50_ Subtract this cost from your $50 and write the amount in "Starting Cash" for Turn 1.
4. What price will you charge? $ _.50_

No. of Inventory	
Starting amount: _250_	**Turn #1** Starting cash:
-10 sold	Income this turn:
End of Turn 1: _240_	Expenses this turn:
-42 sold	Profit this turn: $ 5.00 $ 12.50
	Total in Cash Box: - $ 0
End of Turn 2: _198_	= $ 5.00 + $ 5.00
-45 sold	**Turn #2** Income this turn: = $ 12.50
_153_	Expenses this turn:
_-15_	Profit this turn: $ 21.00
_138_ _138_	Total in Cash Box: - $ 10.00 $ 11.00
_42_	= $ 11.00 + $ 28.50
End of Turn 3:	**Turn #3** Income this turn:
	Expenses this turn: $ 22.50
_96_	Profit this turn: - $ 5.00 $ 17.50
_42_	Total in Cash Box: = $ 17.50 + $ 46.00
	Turn #4 Income this turn:
	Expenses this turn: $ 21.00
_54_	Profit this turn: - $ 10.00 $ 11.00
38 sold	Total in Cash Box: = $ 11.00 + $ 57.00
2 eaten	**Turn #5** Income this turn:
	Expenses this turn: $ 21.00
_14_	Profit this turn: - $ 0 $ 21.00
	Total in Cash Box: = $ 21.00 + $ 78.00
	Turn #6 Income this turn:
	Expenses this turn: $ 19.00
	Profit this turn: - $ 0 $ 19.00
	Total in Cash Box: = $ 19.00 + $ 19.00
	= $ 97.00

- starting amount given to you by Student Council:

— $ 50.00

FINAL PROFIT = $ _47.00_

---

2 A Food Booth at a School Fair

RUNNING A FOOD BOOTH SIMULATION

How much money could you make from a food booth at the school fair? One way to find out is by setting up a simulation. Here you will play a simulation of a food booth. Think about how profit, income, and expenses are related, and how the decisions you make affect profit.

Play the Simulation with the Class

What are the relationships among income, expenses, and profit?

To play this simulation, you will need the following: Setting Up the Food Booth Simulation, Simulation Recording Sheet, Income Results, and Expense Results. Before the class begins playing, complete Setting Up the Food Booth Simulation.

As you play the simulation, think about what decisions you are making as owner of your food booth.

Simulation Rules

1. For each turn, a player rolls two number cubes. The player selects, reads aloud, and crosses off an event from Income Results. Each player records the information on the Simulation Recording Sheet.

2. The player rolls again to select, read aloud, and cross off an event from Expense Results. Each player again records the information on the Simulation Recording Sheet and calculates the profit for the turn. This ends one turn.

3. Players play for six turns, taking turns rolling cubes on each turn. If players roll a number they have already used, they roll again until they get a new number.

Students were surprised at some of the results. One student observed that there could be other variables that weren't in the simulation! "My dad would just give me the money!" she stated. Others commented that they could make more money by investing in more advertising or by having a better location. My students definitely began to think about the variables that affect making a profit in a business! ☐

Students thought it would be a little more fun if they each had a recording sheet and played against their partners. I let students choose their own new prices. They took turns rolling the number cubes and selecting their transactions. This time students had much more knowledge about the game and were able to dive right in with fewer questions! There were fewer errors on the recording sheet. They all came out with completely different results. The goal was to see who got the most profit. ☐

3 Discussing the Simulation Results

Use the following questions to initiate a class discussion focusing on the decisions students made during the simulation and how those decisions affected their profits. This helps students think about the relationship between income, expenses, and profit.

- How much profit did your food booth make? Was this more or less than you expected? How do you think this compares to real businesses?

- What were some of the decisions you made as the owner of your food booth?

- How do you think your decisions affected your income? your expenses? your profit?

- What might you try differently when you play the simulation again? Why?

During the class discussion of the simulation results, listen for students who are trying to do the following: 1) get a sense of some of the decisions a business owner might make; 2) see the difference between income and profit, and how expenses relate to this; 3) describe in their own words the algorithm, Profit = Income − Expenses. Help the class establish a written equation for their descriptions of the algorithm, such as $P = I - E$ or something similar.

4 Playing the Simulation in Pairs

Before students play the simulation again in pairs, make sure that each pair has two number cubes. Give each student a new Simulation Recording Sheet (R10), because it is important for each student to make the calculations. Let students know that the rules remain the same, but that they will need to go through the steps for setting up the simulation again.

Now that students are familiar with the simulation, you might want them to review the Income Results reproducible and Expense Results reproducible to get an idea of the consequences of choosing different prices. When students play the simulation the second time, they have a chance to make some of their decisions differently, and to see how their results affect their profits. This lays the foundation for learning about posing what-if questions, which will be addressed in the next lesson.

5 Comparing the Results of the Two Simulations

After students have written descriptions of their second experience with the simulation, ask volunteers to share their comparisons with the rest of the class.

DO STUDENTS' COMPARISONS:

- *clearly and accurately describe the business decisions made the second time they played the simulation?*
- *show an understanding of how their choices changed the second time they played?*
- *show an understanding of how profits changed the second time and what made them change?*

See *Getting Down to Business* Assessment page A5 for assessment information.

Simulation Recording Sheet

Read Setting Up the Food Booth Simulation to help you answer these questions.

1. Food Item = *popcorn*
2. Number of items bought for inventory = *200*. Write the number in "Starting Amount" at the top of the No. of Inventory column.
3. Total cost of these items = $ *30* Subtract this cost from your $50 and write the amount in "Starting Cash" for Turn 1.
4. What price will you charge? $ *.45*

No. of Inventory		Turn #1
Starting amount: *200*		Starting cash:
End of Turn 1: *105* *190*		Income th: Ex–

decided to lower our inventory, lower cost of cookies from .50¢ to .40¢. It helped! It also helped when the computer club loved our cookies so we had to add 30 additional items to our already sold 36 items.

all of them. We lowered our inventory, lowered our cost and rolled differently. Our second time we played our profit was much more than the first time. Our first time we made $17.90, second time we made $50.70.

...of lowering

Play the Simulation in Pairs

Each pair will need two number cubes and two new Simulation Recording Sheets to play the simulation. To play with a partner, follow the same rules as you did when the class played the simulation.

How do your business decisions affect your profit?

Compare the Results of the Two Simulations

Think about the results of your simulation the second time you played. Describe how your profit changed.

- What decisions did you make the second time you played the simulation? Be sure to tell about the price you chose, how much inventory you bought, what choices you made from the numbers rolled, and any other decisions you made.

- Which of these choices did you make differently the second time?

- How did your final profit compare to your profit the first time you played the simulation?

- Which of your decisions do you think made the biggest difference in your profit the second time? Why?

hot **words** | profit simulation

Homework
page 37

Analyzing the Food Booth Simulation

At first the what-if question did not seem to engage the students, but then they got on task and began to think in terms of a real business. When I gave the recording sheets out to students, they thought everything on the sheets would be different. After a class discussion, they realized that the number of items sold and the expenses would remain the same, and only the price and the profit would change. They also realized that if the price went up and all other variables stayed the same, the profit would go up. They were just beginning to see the relationship between income, expenses, and profit. □

What-If Questions for the Food Booth

1 Reading the Hot Dog Stand Script Follow-Up

Ask a few students to act out the script on Reproducible R13, The Hot Dog Stand (Part 2), or read it aloud in small groups. This script is a follow-up to the script introduced in Lesson 1.

☞ The characters in the script pose questions about how they could have run their booth differently, which lays the groundwork for students to create their own what-if questions in this lesson. Posing such questions is a skill that students will build throughout the unit.

2 Analyzing a Business Decision

student page

Have students choose a new price and recalculate their profits, using the transactions from their second Simulation Recording Sheet in Lesson 2. This will help them begin to learn about posing what-if questions as they investigate the impact of changing the price. You might point out that students do not play the simulation again. When they have finished, have them explain how they calculated the profit to the class.

☞ Determining price is one of the central decisions facing business owners. As students work, they will begin to think about how that business decision affects income, expenses, and profit. This step also demonstrates the kinds of calculations that spreadsheets will perform in the next phase. By taking the time to work through the calculations now, students will better understand and appreciate the power of a spreadsheet. If you feel your students need additional work, you could have them choose another price and repeat the calculations.

homework options

LESSON HOMEWORK

Getting Down to Business
Student Guide page 38
Solutions: Assessment page A31

hot **topics**

- *If/Then Statements*
- *Evaluating Expressions and Formulas*

Analyze a Business Decision

Food item — chocolate chip cookies
bought 250
total cost 37.50
new price .60
sold 234

new income 140.40   234 × .60
expenses   27.50   10 + 5 + 12.50
new profit = 62.90   140.40 − 27.50 − 50.00

---

3 What-If Questions for the Food Booth

ANALYZING THE FOOD BOOTH SIMULATION

What will happen to profit if you charge a different price at your food booth? You can explore different ways of running your food booth simulation by testing how changing price affects profit. See how well you can predict the effects of a price change on income and expenses.

What if you changed the price at your food booth?

Analyze a Business Decision

As you read the script on the handout The Hot Dog Stand Part 2, think about what might have happened if the Hot Dog Stand had been run differently. Choose a different price from the one you used in the simulation. Use the same information that you used in the simulation for how many you sold and how many you bought. Then figure out your profit.

*Students partici-
pated well in the
discussion of their
food booths. For
what to change in their food
booth business, they mentioned
what we sell, cheaper stuff, sell
more, charge more, change loca-
tions, and open more stores. I had
to model changing their sentence-
fragment ideas into what-if questions. After a few false starts, they
began to get the idea! Here are
some of the ways students suggested to change them: sell more
than one thing so people would
have a choice, buy more stuff to
sell, and raise the prices. In terms
of how these changes would affect
income and expenses, students
responded with, "If we sold more
things, people would only have to
stop at one booth and they'd buy
more." "If we found a cheaper
place to buy the stuff, we'd make
more money!"* □

3 Discussing Other Business Decisions

Using questions such as those below, initiate a
class discussion to encourage students to think
about the kinds of business decisions available to
them as owners of a food booth. As students
make suggestions, help them rephrase their suggestions as what-if questions and create a list of
questions on the chalkboard. For example, the
suggestion "I want to buy cheaper supplies for my
booth" can be rephrased as "What if I found supplies that cost me less to buy?"

- What things can you change in your food
  booth business?

- In what ways could you change them?

- How would these changes affect your income
  and expenses?

student page

4 Creating What-If Questions

While students are writing their own what-if
questions, make sure they understand that these
questions are helping them to lay the groundwork for the kinds of questions they will explore
on spreadsheets in the next lesson. Guide students to choose questions that will be suited for
exploration on the spreadsheet—questions that
involve varying a numerical quantity in the
profit-income-expense relationship.

student page

5 Reporting on Profit, Income, and Expenses

As assessment for this phase, ask students to write
a report on profit, income, and expenses for their
food booth. You might want to allow time for
students to share their reports with the class.

At this point in the unit, the emphasis of the
assessment should be on students' ability to identify and calculate income, expenses, and profit.
They should also be able to provide a general explanation
of how changes in income and expenses affect profit, but
their understanding of the profit-income-expense relationship may not be very sophisticated. The work students do here will provide a good basis for comparison
throughout the unit, as students deepen their understanding of how income and expenses interact to determine
profits.

assessment criteria

IN THE REPORTS, DO STUDENTS:

- *identify examples of income and expenses for their food booths?*
- *correctly calculate profit and describe the steps in their own words?*
- *correctly calculate income and describe the steps in their own words?*
- *show an understanding of how changing income and/or expenses will increase profit?*

See *Getting Down to Business* Assessment pages A6–A7 for assessment information.

(Handwritten notes)

1. What if we sold more varieties of cookies?

If we sold more varieties of cookies, our income would probably m... because ... would buy th... ...ase would...

Report Profit, Income, & Expenses

① At my food booth, I sold potato chips. I bought ... bags but I had 59 bags left over. I lost some ... my inventory because a dog ate some and another time someone knocked the bags over. I sold the potato chips for .55 and made a total profit of $53.30.

② Income
5.50 - sold 10 bags
20.90 - sold 38 bags
19.80 - sold 36 bags
23.10 - sold 42 bags
24.75 - sold 45 bags
+ 19.25 - sold 35 bags
113.30

③ Expenses
5 - replace sign
10 - advertising
45
- 60

④ Income - Expenses = Profit
113.30   60 = 53.30

Create What-If Questions

Use the second Simulation Recording Sheet from Lesson 2 to respond to the following:

- List three what-if questions about your food booth.

- For each question, write about whether you think income and expenses will increase or decrease. Be sure to explain your thinking.

How could you pose what-if questions about your own booth?

Report on Profit, Income, and Expenses

Write a short report about how your food booth did at the fair. Your suggestions will be used to plan next year's fair. Include the following in your report:

- a brief description of what happened at your food booth

- a list of your income (Be sure to show how you calculated it.)

- a list of your expenses (Be sure to show how you calculated it.)

- your profit (Be sure to show how you calculated it.)

- three suggestions for making a better profit (Be sure to tell why they will result in a better profit.)

hot **words** | price   what-if questions

Homework

 page 38

A TEACHER REFLECTS

Using Technology in the Classroom

I was more nervous about doing this unit than *any* of my students! Spreadsheets?… I knew how to find one on my computer. That's about it! So I began the journey that so many teachers take of keeping one step ahead of the kids. One of my students asked one of the questions that I, too, wanted to know: Why use a big old computer to do this work when a calculator would do just as well, and it's smaller and fits in my purse? Well, she didn't ask the question in *exactly* the same way, but the meaning was the same! I've learned a lot, along with the students: how to set up a spreadsheet, how to enter a formula, how to identify parts of a spreadsheet, and, most importantly, why I would use a spreadsheet!

The use of so many computers is a challenge that faces all teachers. We need to use technology in our classrooms, but how many of us have continual access to a classroom full of computers? My school has two computer labs that each contain 32 computers. Still, other teachers from departments other than math needed to use them also.

So it was virtually impossible to take my class there for two to three weeks of continual spreadsheet work. I had two computers already in my classroom. I was able to borrow two more from two other math teachers in my school. (They still have techno-phobia and seldom used them anyway!) The computer lab technician loaned me a mobile computer that hooks up to a large monitor. Finally, I happened to mention to the director of the Northern California Math Project at UC Davis that I had a problem getting enough computers for this project, and she loaned me three more computers for the duration of the unit! I found that a classroom with eight computers is manageable and actually a better situation than going to a lab. Students didn't have to wait for a schedule to use them and could ask to go to the computer any time they wanted. The only thing better would be to have a computer at every desk, but I suppose that's somewhere in the future. In the meantime, I'll look for a grant to have eight computers in my classroom all the time!

Spreadsheets

Students learn what spreadsheets are and the mechanics of using them before creating spreadsheets on the computer.

AT A GLANCE

LESSON 4

What-If Questions on Spreadsheets

This is the first of two lessons introducing the spreadsheet. In this lesson, students focus on the *purpose* of a spreadsheet as a tool for exploring how different business decisions affect profit. They investigate several what-if questions for a business. An optional investigation with the calculator is provided for students to work on when they do not have access to a computer.

Mathematical Goals

- Understand the purpose of a spreadsheet as a problem-solving tool.

- Pose and investigate what-if questions on the spreadsheet and a calculator.

- Enter information into a spreadsheet.

- Read information in a table.

MATERIALS

PER STUDENT

- calculator

- Reproducible R17 (optional)

PREPARATION

Students need access to computers that have a spreadsheet program. See page vii. Make a transparency of Reproducibles R14–R16. Make a spreadsheet template for each pair of students, using the information on pages 30–31.

LESSON 5

"What's My Formula?" Game

Students play a game on the computer that involves mathematical formulas and the mechanics of spreadsheet notation. In the game, each student must figure out a partner's hidden spreadsheet formula. As students enter and search for formulas, they find ways of writing notation so that spreadsheets will accept the instruction. After playing the game, students reflect on the purpose of spreadsheet formulas and suggest ways of helping others to use and understand spreadsheets.

Mathematical Goals

- Learn to read and write formulas written in spreadsheet notation.

- Given two numbers, find a formula that inputs one number and yields the other.

- Apply knowledge of order of operations to spreadsheet calculations.

MATERIALS

PER STUDENT

- calculator

- Reproducible R18 (optional)

PREPARATION

Students will need access to computers that have a spreadsheet program. See page vii. Familiarize yourself with how to write formulas in spreadsheet notation for your spreadsheet application.

LESSON 6

Double Your Profits?

Students create a spreadsheet on the computer and use it to explore ways to make their food booth more profitable. They set up the formulas for the spreadsheet on paper first and then transfer the information to the computer. After they explore their own what-if questions, they write about their top recommendation for doubling profit. The lesson ends with the phase assessment of students' understanding of spreadsheets and formulas.

Mathematical Goals

- Create a spreadsheet to use as a mathematical model for the simulation.

- Create formulas in spreadsheet notation.

- Pose and explore what-if questions on the spreadsheet.

- Make a recommendation based on data from the spreadsheet exploration.

MATERIALS

PER STUDENT

- calculator

PREPARATION

Students will need access to computers that have a spreadsheet program. See page vii. Make sure students have their Simulation Recording Sheets from the second time they played the simulation in Lesson 2. Students should work with their original partner from Lesson 2, so that they can pose what-if questions that apply to the same data.

TECHNOLOGY OPTIONS

Spreadsheet Basics

A spreadsheet is a table of information with rows and columns in which you can perform calculations using that information. For example, this spreadsheet shows ticket sales for a movie theater.

	A	B	C	D
1		**Number of Tickets**	**Price**	**Income**
2	Movie 1	150	$7	$1,050
3	Movie 2	250	$7	$1,750
4	Movie 3	300	$7	$2,100
5				
6	TOTAL	700		$4,900

Entering Information in a Spreadsheet

Each rectangle in a spreadsheet is called a **cell.** Cells are referred to by a letter and a number that indicate the column and the row, respectively. In the spreadsheet above, the number 700 is in cell B6.

In any cell, you can enter one of three kinds of information: text, numbers, or formulas. Click on the desired cell, and type in the information. Information is entered in a cell once you select any other cell, or press the RETURN key on your keyboard.

To enter text or numbers, simply type them in. At the top of the spreadsheet is a formula bar. Anything you type will appear both in the cell and in this formula bar, but you may edit what you typed only in the formula bar.

To enter a formula in any spreadsheet, you must begin the formula with a specified symbol. In most spreadsheet applications, you must begin the formula with an equal sign (=), though some applications may require a plus sign (+) or other symbol. In the spreadsheet shown at left, the number in B6 was the result of typing the formula =B2+B3+B4 into cell B6. Whatever values are in B2, B3, and B4 will be added, and the sum will appear in B6. Note that the formula will appear in the cell only while you are typing it in. However, once you enter this information in the cell, the result of the formula will appear in the cell; the formula will still appear in the formula bar.

Spreadsheets use the asterisk symbol (*) to indicate multiplication, and the forward slash symbol (/) to indicate division. In the spreadsheet shown, the number in D2 was the result of multiplying the number of tickets by the price. The formula typed in cell D2 was =B2*C2.

Setting Up a Spreadsheet Template

Before Lesson 4, you will need to set up a spreadsheet template on the computer and make a copy of the template for each pair of students. The final template will look like this:

	A	B	C	D	E	F	G
1	Booth	Number Sold	Price	Income	Cost per Item	Expenses	Profit
2	Potato Chips	600	$0.30	$180.00	$0.15	$90.00	$90.00
3	Chocolate Chip Cookies	750	$0.40	$300.00	$0.15	$112.50	$187.50
4	Popcorn	800	$0.30	$240.00	$0.15	$120.00	$120.00
5	Total Profit						$397.50

To create this spreadsheet, type in the following information:

	A	B	C	D	E	F	G
1	Booth	Number Sold	Price	Income	Cost per Item	Expenses	Profit
2	Potato Chips	600	$0.30	=B2*C2	$0.15	=B2*E2	=D2−F2
3	Chocolate Chip Cookies	750	$0.40	=B3*C3	$0.15	=B3*E3	=D3−F3
4	Popcorn	800	$0.30	=B4*C4	$0.15	=B4*E4	=D4−E4
5	Total Profit						=G2+G3+G4

4

Understanding the Purpose of Spreadsheets

The discussion went quickly. Most students were familiar with rows and columns. On the overhead, I outlined some cells for students with an overhead projector pen. Then I asked them to name the cell I had outlined, making sure that students gave the letter of the column first and the number of the row last, such as B2, C5, etc. ☐

Some students were confused. When asked where they would find all the information about popcorn, some students responded in cell A3! Some students listed all the cells individually. Others got the idea that they could name a row or column for some of the questions! This gave them an opportunity to learn from each other. ☐

What-If Questions on Spreadsheets

Have students review the phase overview on pages 12–13 in the Student Guide.

1 Discussing a Spreadsheet

After students have read the description of a spreadsheet, discuss these elements of a spreadsheet with the class: row, column, and cell. Make sure students realize that if they type something in a cell, it will appear in the formula bar first.

> The main purpose of this lesson is to help students understand a spreadsheet: what a spreadsheet is, how it is related to tables, and how it can be used to explore what-if questions. Students will expand their understanding of spreadsheets throughout this phase as they work with their own spreadsheets.

student page

2 Investigating Profit on a Spreadsheet

On the overhead projector, display the transparency Profit Made by the Food Booths (R14) and overlay it with the transparency Sample Numbers to Start (R15). Make sure students understand that the numbers shown are initial data. Explain to the class that a spreadsheet helps to organize information into a table. After students have responded to the questions, have several volunteers show the location of the answers on the overhead. See Assessment page A25 for more information.

> In the Lesson 2 simulation, students subtracted the cost of the items from their initial $50. In this spreadsheet, students subtract the cost of the items directly as part of the calculation of profit. Students should also be aware that there are other expenses not included here that come up in the simulation, such as repairs, salaries, and advertising.

3 Discussing What-If Questions for a Spreadsheet

Overlay the transparency What If the Booths Sold More? (R16) with the transparency Profit Made by the Food Booths. Using questions such as these, help students think about which values would have to be recalculated if the booths sold more.

- Which columns would have to be recalculated? Why?

- How did the values in each cell change?

- Did you notice any patterns in these changes? Explain what you observed.

> Emphasize that a spreadsheet can help students explore different what-if questions by recalculating some of the numbers for them each time they pose a different question. In this example, each number in the "Number Sold" column is 100 more than the original sample numbers. That means income is recalculated. Because income changes, profit is also recalculated. This will help students see the advantage that spreadsheets have

hot **topics**

• *Spreadsheets*
• *Four-Function Calculator*

1. I would find information about Popcorn in row 5. I would find information on Potato chips in row 3.
2. I would find information for expenses in Column F. I would find the price in Column C. The income would be in column D.
3. You would find the total profit in cell G6. You would find the number of chocolate chip cookies in Cell B 4.

4 What-If Questions on Spreadsheets

UNDERSTANDING
THE PURPOSE OF
SPREADSHEETS

You can use a computer spreadsheet that has been set up with certain formulas to calculate profit, income, and expenses. In this lesson, you will explore what-if questions on a spreadsheet. This will help you to see how business decisions affect profit.

Investigate Profit on a Spreadsheet

How can you use a spreadsheet?

A **spreadsheet** is organized into a grid of rows and columns. **Rows** are horizontal and numbered along the left side. **Columns** are vertical and labeled across the top of the spreadsheet with letters. Each small rectangle is called a **cell**. Cells are where you place information or data in your spreadsheet. Look over the spreadsheet containing data on this page and answer these questions:

1 Where would you find all the information about popcorn? potato chips?

2 Where would you find all the information for expenses? for price? for income?

3 Where would you find the total profit? the number of chocolate chip cookies sold?

Profit Made by the Food Booths						
	A	**B**	**C**	**D**	**E**	**F**	**G**
1							
2	**Booth**	**No. Sold**	**Price**	**Income**	**Cost per Item**	**Expenses**	**Profit**
3	Potato Chips	400	$0.30	$120.00	$0.15	$60.00	$60.00
4	Chocolate Chip Cookies	450	$0.40	$180.00	$0.15	$67.50	$112.50
5	Popcorn	600	$0.30	$180.00	$0.15	$90.00	$90.00
6	TOTALS						$262.50

GETTING DOWN TO BUSINESS LESSON 4
14 © Creative Publications • MathScape

When we went into the computer lab, I found my students wanted time to just play around and explore what the spreadsheet could do. I wasn't sure that this would be useful. In retrospect, I now think they needed that time and learned something from free exploration. Next time, I will try giving them some questions to guide their thinking about how a spreadsheet works to structure their free exploration time. □

Some of my students caught on quickly and had an easy time working through the questions. When they were done, I suggested they go back and replace the template data with data from their own food booth and then try out some of the what-if questions they wrote in the last lesson. □

4 Using a Spreadsheet

After students read through the tips for using a spreadsheet, you might want to demonstrate the key ideas on a computer to small groups. Suggest that students refer to these tips to help them access and use the spreadsheet when they have time on the computer.

5 Exploring What-If Questions on a Spreadsheet

student page

Have pairs of students work at the computer using the spreadsheet template you have prepared to explore the what-if questions (see page 31). Be aware that the data in the template is slightly different from the data students worked with in Step 2. Pairs could take turns typing at the computer and recording the responses to the questions. If a printer is available, you might want students to print the spreadsheet and highlight the responses to each question.

When students are waiting to use the computer or have finished on the computer, you can refer them to Reproducible R17, Finding Profit Using a Calculator. This will help students think about the effects of different what-if questions on the relationship between income, expenses, and profit, and deepen their understanding of the mathematical relationship, but it is not essential. See Assessment page A25 for more information.

As students explore what-if questions on the computer, they will begin to get a sense of how to use a spreadsheet as a problem-solving tool. Students change different values on the spreadsheet to find what happens to total profit, but do not enter any formulas. This may be a new and challenging concept for many students. Some students may need extra guidance in thinking about which values will change and how the spreadsheet can do the recalculations. Watch for these students, who may do all their calculations on a calculator and simply enter the results on the spreadsheet, avoiding the use of any formulas.

what to look for

CAN STUDENTS:

- *use a spreadsheet on the computer properly?*
- *understand how to change the data on a spread-sheet in response to a what-if question?*
- *find out what happens to total profit using the spreadsheet?*

See *Getting Down to Business* Assessment page A9 for assessment information.

Recordings

Item   NO. SOLD   PROFIT

Chips
Cookies   1200
Popcorn   1500
Total

Exploring what-if questions on a spreadsheet

The number sold of potato chips would be 1200, the number of chocolate chip cookies sold would be 1500, and then the number of popcorn sold would be 1600. The profit for potato chips would be $180, for chocolate chip cookies $375, and for popcorn $240. The total profit would be $795.

The number sold of potato chips...

Explore What-If Questions on a Spreadsheet

Use the spreadsheet on the computer to change the numbers described in each what-if question below.

How can you use a spreadsheet to explore what-if questions?

1 What if each booth sells double the amount shown on the spreadsheet? Record the information in the Number Sold and Profit columns. Record the Total Profit.

2 What if each booth sells half as many items? Record the information in the Number Sold and Profit columns. Record the Total Profit.

3 What if the expenses for each booth double? Record the information in the Expenses and Profit columns. Record the Total Profit.

4 What if nobody buys potato chips and you bought 600 bags of chips? Record the information in the Number Sold and Profit columns. Record the Total Profit.

5 What if you raised your prices by 10 cents? Record the information in the Price and Profit columns. Record the Total Profit.

6 What if you raised your prices by 15 cents and your cost per item went up by 15 cents? Record the information in the Price, Expenses, and Profit columns. Record the Total Profit.

Tips for Using a Spreadsheet

- Find out the name of the file for your spreadsheet and open it.

- To change information in a cell, click the cell to select it. Type your changes into the formula bar and press RETURN.

- Remember to save the file before you close the spreadsheet, so that you don't lose your data.

hot words | spreadsheet cells

Homework

page 39

5

Understanding the Mechanics of Spreadsheets

As practice for writing formulas, I played a game with my students. I pointed to a cell and they had to say the cell reference, tell whether the number was entered by hand or calculated by the computer, and if computed, tell what the algorithm was in spreadsheet language. □

My students were confused about the difference between entering a number in a cell and assigning a formula to a cell. I explained that the "=" tells the computer, "Okay, now I'm (student) going to tell you (computer) what to compute and then you should put that answer in this cell, instead of just the numbers and letters I am typing in." □

"What's My Formula?" Game

1 Discussing Formulas

Using questions such as the following, have a class discussion about what students already know about formulas. Help students think about a formula as a generalized set of directions. This will prepare them to understand how formulas are used in a spreadsheet.

- What is a formula?

- What formulas do you already know?

- What kinds of calculations does a business owner need to do repeatedly?

- What kinds of formulas might you use as a business owner?

Students may give examples of mathematical formulas that they are familiar with, such as the perimeter of a rectangle, but they may not think of nonmathematical examples, such as the recipe for making lemonade. You might need to suggest some nonmathematical analogies to help students think about formulas. Both types of examples help students articulate a clearer image of a formula.

student page

2 Writing Formulas in Spreadsheet Notation

After students have read over the guidelines, discuss them with the class. You may want to show the class several examples of formulas written in spreadsheet notation. When students have finished writing their formulas, ask them to share the formulas they wrote with the class. Make sure students understand spreadsheet notation before they play the game in the next step. See Assessment page A25 for more information.

Students explore mathematical formulas in this lesson by learning spreadsheet notation. Spreadsheet notation is a specific type of mathematical formula with its own syntax. As students come to understand the use of formulas to express mathematical relationships generally, they will understand the power of the spreadsheet as a tool for problem solving.

homework options

LESSON HOMEWORK

Getting Down to Business
Student Guide page 40
Solutions: Assessment page A33

hot topics

- *Spreadsheets*
- *Order of Operations*

1. Cell D3 would have the formula B3 * C3. This formula tells you how much money came in to the booth, or the INCOME.

2. Cell G4 would have the formula D4 - F4 in it. This formula tells you how much money the booth made, or the PROFIT.

3. Income for the popcorn booth: = B5 * C5.
   Profit for the chocolate chip cookies booth: =D4 - F4.
   Total profit = G3 + G4 + G5.

---

5 "What's My Formula?" Game

UNDERSTANDING
THE MECHANICS OF
SPREADSHEETS

The secret to the power of a spreadsheet is in writing the formulas that make the calculations for you. Here you will play a game on the computer that will help you learn how to write formulas in spreadsheet notation. Can you figure out your partner's hidden formula?

How do you write formulas for a spreadsheet?

Write Formulas in Spreadsheet Notation

Read the guidelines below. Use the Profit Made by the Food Booths on page 14 to understand formulas in spreadsheets and answer these questions:

1 What cell would have the formula $=B3*C3$ in it? What information in the spreadsheet does this formula give you?

2 What cell would have the formula $=D4-F4$ in it? What information in the spreadsheet does this formula give you?

3 Write a spreadsheet formula that could make the calculation for each of the following: income for the popcorn booth, profit for the chocolate chip cookies booth, and total profit.

Guidelines for Writing Spreadsheet Formulas

- Each cell has a letter and a number. For example, the cell in the upper left corner is named A1.

- In a spreadsheet, you use an asterisk ($*$) to multiply. For example, $2*3$.

- In a spreadsheet, you use a forward slash (/) to divide. For example, $16/4$.

- Formulas in spreadsheet notation usually begin with an $=$ sign. (Some may use a $+$ sign instead.) An example is $=B4-7$. One way to think about this is that you select a cell and then press $=$ to tell the computer, "Make cell A1 equal to the answer to this equation."

*Sometimes my students forgot to include the cell reference in their expression. They expressed the formula "= B2 * 3" as "= * 3." The computer gave them the message, Error in Formula, but they needed some help in understanding what they had omitted. □*

After playing the game as a whole class, students were ready to play the formula game in pairs. I heard cries of "You forgot to say equal!" and "Use asterisk, not times!" □

student page

3 Playing a Formula Game

Explain the rules for the formula game to the class and use a computer to demonstrate how the spreadsheet automatically recalculates values. As partners play the game on the computer, they will get automatic feedback about whether or not they have entered a formula correctly, because the computer will not calculate a formula until it is correctly entered in spreadsheet notation. Observe students to find out if they are using cell references and spreadsheet notation correctly.

When students are waiting to use the computer or have finished on the computer, you can distribute Reproducible R18, Getting to 25. Although Getting to 25 is not essential, it provides opportunities for students to read and write spreadsheet notation, and to write expressions using the correct order of operations. See Assessment page A26 for more information.

Some questions about equivalent expressions may arise as students play the game. For example, a student who enters the formula "= (A1 + 2) * 5" may think of this formula as having two steps: adding 2 and multiplying by 5. A partner may argue that the formula has different steps: multiplying by 5 and adding 10. Students are then equating $(x + 2) * 5$ with $5x + 10$, and may need help seeing that these expressions are equivalent.

4 Discussing Formulas in Spreadsheets

To help students understand the mathematical power of expressing a relationship in a spreadsheet, discuss with the class questions such as those that follow. By the end of the discussion, check to see if students understand that by using a formula with cell references, a spreadsheet can calculate mathematical relationships with any numbers that are in the cells.

- If "Income" was in cell D2 and "Expenses" was in cell F2, how would you write a formula for profit using spreadsheet notation?

- Why would the formula for profit use cell references instead of the numbers in those cells?

- Why would you use a formula in a spreadsheet?

student page

5 Sharing About Spreadsheet Formulas

After students have written their tips for using a spreadsheet, bring the class together to compile the tips for reference throughout the unit.

what to look for

CAN STUDENTS:

- *write tips that are useful to someone who wants to use a spreadsheet?*
- *include tips that were based on something that was confusing before?*
- *write tips that are clear and easy to understand for a novice?*

See *Getting Down to Business* Assessment page A9 for assessment information.

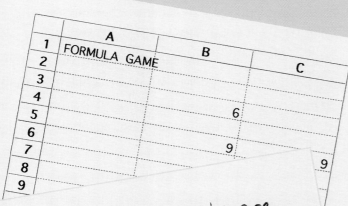

I learned that spreadsheets are complicated when Sometimes it is complicated when you don't use a spreadsheet on a computer.

There was only one thing confusing to me. Formulas. They are hard because sometimes you forget to put the equals (=) sign in it. To make it less confusing I just listen in class.

When using a spreadsheet you should always _ _ teacher. Sometimes the spreadsheet _ _ _ used. That

---

Play a Formula Game

You and your partner will need a computer with a spreadsheet to play this game.

Can you figure out your partner's hidden formula?

Rules for "What's My Formula?"

Player A will make formulas, and Player B will guess hidden formulas. Decide who will be Players A and B. Players switch roles after several rounds.

1. Player B's eyes are closed while Player A enters a number into a cell.

	A	B	C
1			
2		6	
3			
4			

2. In any other cell, Player A enters a formula that uses the cell of the number just entered.

	A	B	C
1			
2		6	
3			
4			=B2+7

3. Player A presses RETURN or clicks the box. This will appear on the spreadsheet.

	A	B	C
1			
2		6	
3			
4			13

4. Player B tries to discover the formula. Player B can only change the number in the first cell where Player A entered a number.

	A	B	C
1			
2		→6	
3			
4			13

5. Player B checks an idea by entering it as a formula in a different cell and comparing answers. If they are the same, the formula is correct. Player B prints the spreadsheet.

	A	B	C
1			
2		6	
3			
4	=B2+7		13

Share About Spreadsheet Formulas

Write several tips for someone using a spreadsheet for the first time. Consider these questions:

- What did you learn about a spreadsheet that you didn't know before?

- What was confusing to you? What suggestions do you have for making it less confusing?

- What other helpful tips do you have about using a spreadsheet?

hot **words** | formula / cells

Homework

page 40

GETTING DOWN TO BUSINESS LESSON 5
© Creative Publications • MathScape **17**

6

LESSON

Creating a Spreadsheet to Double Profits

Some of my students became very focused on doubling their profits, and started losing sight of the what-if questions they were exploring. As a result, they began varying more than one quantity, sometimes randomly adjusting the numbers to get as close as possible. I reminded them that they should be able to isolate the what-if question and the numbers they used to explore their question. As students tried to explain what change gave them doubled profit, they realized their mistakes. □

Double Your Profits?

An overview of this phase for students appears on pages 4–5 of the Student Guide.

1 Planning and Creating a Spreadsheet

Ask students to use Simulation Recording Sheets from Lesson 2 to build tables for their spreadsheets on paper. Then have them transfer the information from the tables to a spreadsheet on the computer. You might suggest that students refer to the Tips for Using a Spreadsheet in Lesson 4.

The two tables that students produce help them translate information from the Simulation Recording Sheets into a format that will guide the work they do as they set up their spreadsheets on the computer. This is the first of three times in the unit that students create their own spreadsheets. They are given more structure in the beginning, and less in later lessons as they become more familiar with spreadsheets. Because this step and the next one require a large amount of computer time, you could assign homework to students who are not using the computer.

2 Doubling Profits on a Spreadsheet

Before students explore different ways to double their food booth profits on the spreadsheet, decide whether they will work individually or in pairs. If students work in pairs, ask them to take turns typing at the computer and highlighting changes on their printed copy.

In this step students should actually see the real power of a spreadsheet. Many students will be amazed at how quickly the spreadsheet can calculate and show results. This might be a good opportunity to discuss the advantages of using spreadsheets in running a business.

LESSON HOMEWORK

Getting Down to Business
Student Guide page 41
Solutions: Assessment page A34

hot topics

- *Spreadsheets*
- *If/Then Statements*

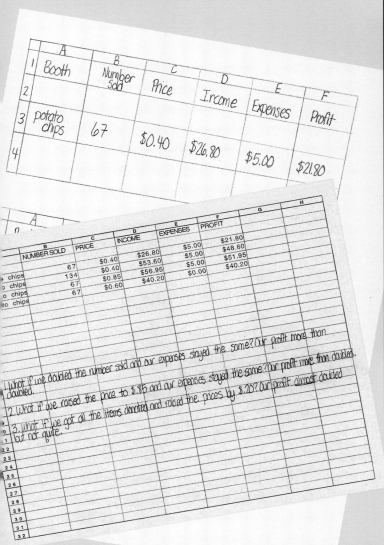

Double Your Profits?

CREATING A SPREADSHEET TO DOUBLE PROFITS

How could you double your profits for your food booth?
You can use what you have learned about spreadsheets to explore ways to increase your profits. Organizing information, posing what-if questions, and analyzing data will help you find ways to double profits.

How could you double your profit for your food booth?

Double Profits on a Spreadsheet

After you have planned your spreadsheet on paper, enter it into the computer. Use the spreadsheet you create on the computer to find three different ways you could double the profit of your simulation. For each way that you find, complete the following tasks:

- Write about it in the form of a what-if question.
- Keep track of what happens to income, expenses, and profit.
- Print the spreadsheet that shows the results.

Steps for Planning a Spreadsheet

1. Make two tables with the following column headings: Booth, Number Sold, Price, Income, Expenses, and Profit.

2. In the first table, enter the data from one of the turns on your Simulation Recording Sheet. Make sure you enter the food item you chose in the booth column.

3. Figure out the appropriate formulas using spreadsheet notation for income, expenses, and profit.

4. In the second table, enter these formulas in the correct cells.

GETTING DOWN TO BUSINESS   LESSON 6
18   © Creative Publications • MathScape

Students had good ideas about doubling their profits, but were surprised that some of their what-if questions resulted in less than a doubling or even more than a doubling of their profits. Some of my students voluntarily stayed after school to explore their spreadsheets some more! Others asked to work in the computer lab at lunch time. Some of them were definitely hooked! When they entered their formulas correctly, they were able to really see the power of the "fill down" feature of their spreadsheet. ▫

We discussed the analysis of the spreadsheets, and students seemed excited and sometimes even frustrated by what they learned. The biggest surprise for them came at their ability to finally make a spreadsheet by themselves. Almost all of them could ask me for permission to go make a spreadsheet by themselves and could do it. I felt as if I could finally take off my roller-skates and actually walk around the room! ▫

3 Analyzing Your Business

student page

After students have written a description of how they doubled their profit and made their business recommendations, ask them to share their ideas with the class. Questions such as the following can help to further students' understanding of the relationships among profit, income, and expenses.

- Did you change the income as one way to double your profit? If so, how?

- Did you change the expenses as one way to double your profit? If so, how?

- What can you say about the relationships among profit, income, and expenses? Use math in your explanation.

This provides an opportunity for students to make recommendations based on their data. Listen to see that students use their data to back up their recommendations rather than relying solely on intuition. You might also listen to the ways students are using the terms profit, income, cost, and expenses. You could ask students to revise and add to the list of business terms on the chart started in Lesson 1.

4 Analyzing Your Spreadsheet

student page

Ask students to read through and complete an analysis of their spreadsheets, making sure they attach copies of their spreadsheets. This work serves to assess students' understanding about spreadsheets and formulas in this phase. You might consider having students look over each other's work.

When students look over each other's work, they can gain insights into their classmates' thinking and see the value of different strategies. This should not be a substitute for the teacher's assessment of the work, but would enhance the assessment process, because it gives students the chance to offer positive, constructive feedback on each other's work.

DO THE STUDENTS' SPREADSHEET ANALYSES INCLUDE:

- *formulas written correctly in spreadsheet notation?*
- *an explanation of what a formula is and, in general, when and where to use one?*
- *clearly written what-if questions and an understandable explanation of the meaning of a what-if question?*

See *Getting Down to Business* Assessment pages A10–A11 for assessment information.

ANALYZING YOUR BUSINESS

• The three ways I doubled my profit is...
    1. Doubled...
    2...

LYZE YOUR SPREADSHEET

COLUMNS- booth, number sold , price, income, expenses, fit.
WS-potato chips
FORMULAS
COME =B4*C4 etc. Income= number sold times price
ROFIT =D4-E4 etc. Profit = income minus expenses

We used formulas in cells where you had to use numbers in other columns to get the answer.

A formula is a way of telling the computer to use numbers from other cells to find the answer. When you put a number in a cell, you have to change it yourself if you want to try a different problem. But if you put a formula in a cell the number will change for you.

2. What if we tripled the number sold and the expenses were the same? What if we raised the price and the expenses went up? What if we reduced our expenses and increased the price?

3. Someone could just use our spreadsheet and change the cells in the question. If you tripled the number sold, you would multiply each number in the number sold column by 3. Then you would see what happens to income, expenses and profit.

Analyze Your Business

Use the information you gathered on the computer about doubling profits to answer these questions:

1 Describe the three ways you doubled your profit.

2 As a business owner, which way would you recommend for doubling your profit? Why?

What would you recommend for your business?

Analyze Your Spreadsheet

Spend a few minutes reflecting on what you have learned about spreadsheets and formulas.

1 Use these questions to help you write about how you set up your spreadsheet:

   a. What columns and rows did you put on your spreadsheet?

   b. What formulas did you put into your spreadsheet?

   c. How did you decide which cells should have formulas?

   d. How would you explain to someone what a formula is?

2 Write three different what-if questions you could explore on your spreadsheet.

3 How would someone else test one of the what-if questions on your spreadsheet?

4 Attach a copy of your spreadsheet to your work.

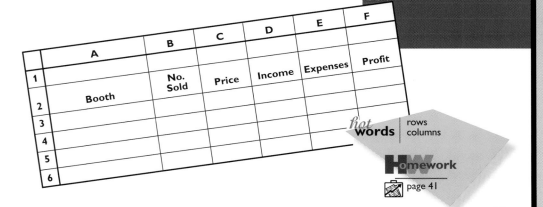

	A	B	C	D	E	F
1		No. Sold	Price	Income	Expenses	Profit
2	Booth					
3						
4						
5						
6						

hot **words**   rows columns

Homework
page 41

GETTING DOWN TO BUSINESS LESSON 6
© Creative Publications • MathScape   **19**

A TEACHER REFLECTS

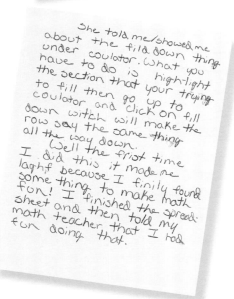

I'm a 8th grade student working with spreedsheets for the friot time. I became very frustated with spreedsheets when I couldn't find a easy way to make them make sence to me. so I started to hate math I went up and told my teacher that I hated math, but I didn't hate her just what subject she thought.
I went back over to the comuter and starded to type up the spreedsheet that I had finished writing out. Eventuly I went over to mrs.Lasly's (my math teacher) and asked if there was an easy way to make an enter row say the same thing.

She told me/showed me about the fild down thing under coulator. What you have to do is high-light the section that your trying to fill then go up to coulator and click on fill down witch will make the row say the same thing all the way down.
Well the friot time I did this it made me laghf because I finily found some thing to make math fun! I finished the spread-sheet and then told my math teacher that I had fun doing that.

Formulas in Spreadsheets?

This was the phase in the unit where my students first encountered formulas. I soon found out that they had preconceived notions of what a formula is and how it should look. They also noticed that a formula looks a little different on a spreadsheet. *I found that out myself!*

Students would typically forget to type in the equal sign ($=$) before they entered the formula into the cell. I played the What's My Formula? Game with the class before students played it with their partners. They told me what to do. If they did not say "equal" first, I did not write anything down. I just stood there quietly. The students would look at me and say, "She's not writing anything." Soon a few students would say, "Equals! You forgot to say equals!" I would then continue to write the rest of the formula. The more I thought about why some students were confused about formulas, the more I realized that maybe it was because I wasn't clear about spreadsheet formulas and I needed to work through that.

Students really loved learning about the "fill down" option available on the computer to enter formulas. One special education student wrote the report shown which explains the concept of fill down, and is a wonderful commentary on the positive influence the unit had on this student's attitude toward math.

Doubling Profit

In Lesson 6, some of the students just agonized over getting *exactly* double the profit. I realized that we had to talk some common sense, so I asked, "Do you think a business person would mind if she went a little over double?" This helped students understand that an approximation was not only sometimes mathematically acceptable, but could be applied to the real world as well. Then as long as these students got a little more than double, they felt comfortable.

To double profit, some students used the "guess and check" method. They would write down some numbers and then go to the spreadsheet on the computer to check their numbers. When that didn't work, students would brainstorm with their partner about why and what to try next. This was acceptable to me because I think a great deal of learning occurs when students go back and revise their work. It is like the scientific method where students would make a conjecture, and the spreadsheet on the computer would prove or disprove it!

SPREADSHEET TO SHOW T-SHIRT SALES

PRICE NUMBER EXPENSES INCOME PROFIT
       SOLD

$12.00   25 $100.00 $300.00 $200.00
$13.00   24 $100.00 $312.00 $212.00
$15.00   23 $100.00 $345.00 $245.00
$16.00 $100.00 $245.00
$17.00 $100.00
$18.00   21 $100.00 $378.00 $278.00
$19.00   20 $100.00 $380.00 $280.00
$20.00   17 $100.00 $340.00 $240.00
$21.00   16 $100.00 $336.00 $236.00
$22.00   16 $100.00 $352.00 $252.00
          .00 $100.00
$24.00   13 $100.00 $3

PHASE THREE

Spreadsheets and Graphs

Students use graphs and spreadsheets to continue their investigation of the relationships among price, income, and profit.

LESSON 7

How Many Sales at Tee-Time?

This lesson is the first of three in which students serve as consultants to the Tee-Time T-Shirt Company. Students begin thinking about how to use graphs as tools for analyzing functional relationships. The class makes a table using the data gathered from a survey of students in the class about the price people are willing to pay for T-shirts. After plotting the data on a graph, students explore relationships among the points and between the two axes of the graph: price and the number of people who would buy T-shirts.

Mathematical Goals

- Organize data in a table.

- Plot data points on a graph.

- Explore relationships among points and axes on a graph.

- Use graphs to make recommendations.

MATERIALS

PER STUDENT

- Reproducible R19 or R20

PER CLASS

- chart paper

PREPARATION

To record students' responses in the class survey, make a blank table on chart paper, as shown on page 51. In the price column, list prices in $1 increments ranging from $12 to $24. Save this table for Lesson 8.

LESSON 8

How Much Profit at Tee-Time?

Students continue their investigation into Tee-Time's pricing questions, using spreadsheets and graphs. Students create a spreadsheet to explore the effect of price and number of sales on expenses and income, and therefore on profit. They use the results from their spreadsheet investigation to create graphs showing the relationships between price and income, price and expenses, and price and profit. As students analyze and compare the shapes of these graphs, they strengthen their understanding of the relationships among profit, income, and expenses.

Mathematical Goals

- Use a spreadsheet to investigate the relationship between price and profit.

- Relate data from a spreadsheet to data from a line graph.

- Use graphs to represent and analyze functional relationships.

- Pose what-if questions about price and profit.

- Organize information into a table.

MATERIALS

PER STUDENT

- calculator

- Reproducible R21 (optional)

PREPARATION

Display the class survey table created in Lesson 7. Students will need access to computers that have a spreadsheet program. See page vii.

LESSON 9

Months Later at Tee-Time

As consultants, students generate a graph without numbers for Tee-Time that shows profit. Then students review and complete sets of qualitative graphs that show the general trends without specific numbers for profits, income, and expenses over time. This requires students to apply their knowledge of the functional relationships among profit, income, and expenses more abstractly. The lesson ends with the phase assessment, in which students explain the relationships represented in sets of qualitative graphs.

Mathematical Goals

- Relate qualitative and quantitative graphs.

- Create and interpret qualitative graphs to understand the profit-income-expenses relationship.

- Combine information from two graphs to create a third.

- Describe in general terms the relationships among income, expenses, and profit.

MATERIALS

PER STUDENT

- Reproducible R22

MATH BACKGROUND

In this phase, students generate two different kinds of graphs: scatter plot graphs and qualitative line graphs.

The *scatter plot graphs* that appear in Lessons 7 and 8 show discrete amounts, with finite sets of numbers in the domain and in the range of the function. For example, in Lesson 7, the number of T-shirts can only be represented by integers because you cannot have fractional T-shirts. Similarly, the smallest increment possible for a price on this graph would be 1¢ because it makes no sense to take prices to the thousandths place or smaller. A line graph in which the points were connected would mistakenly convey that for any price along the *x*-axis, even those with fractional numbers of cents, there would be a corresponding fractional number of T-shirts that could be sold at that price.

Even though the points should not be connected by lines, the trend in the direction of the points gives information about the relationship between the two amounts being graphed. Some graphs will show a direct relationship: as one amount increases, so does the other, as with number sold and income. Other graphs may show an indirect relationship: as one amount increases, the other decreases, as with increasing prices resulting in fewer items sold.

However, in order to show trends, businesses often use line graphs with no numbers on the axes, and that is the intent of the *qualitative graphs* in Lesson 9. Removing numbers from the axes allows the graphs to accurately represent

trends, so that students can focus on describing the relationship. For instance, suppose one graph shows income remaining constant over time, and a second graph shows increasing expenses. These two graphs together suggest that a graph of profit over time would show profits decreasing. Focusing on the relationship between profit, income, and expenses at this general level gives students a visual way to understand the nature of this function and to understand what it means for sets of numbers to be mathematically related to each other.

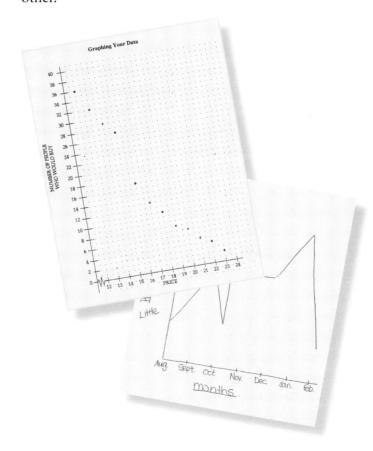

TECHNOLOGY OPTIONS

A Note About Graphs and Spreadsheets

Most spreadsheet applications have commands that allow the user to create a variety of types of graphs from a selected set of data. Though the unit uses line graphs, the authors have chosen not to present graphing concepts using spreadsheet applications because of the complexity in doing so.

Each time the data is changed, the spreadsheet application redraws the graph to reflect these changes, and the axes of the graph are recalibrated. It is possible to override this and fix the axes, but it is often quite complicated to do so, and the teacher would have to set it up carefully ahead of time. Graphs that have constantly changing axes are extremely confusing for students who do not have a thorough grasp of the purpose of a linear graph. Comparisons between graphs are difficult to make.

Common Mistakes Students Make Using Spreadsheets

- Students may inadvertently scroll to the right by accidentally clicking in the horizontal scroll bar, and find their spreadsheet apparently blank. Click on the left arrow on the horizontal scroll bar to make sure the left margin of the spreadsheet is at the left edge of the screen.

- Students may forget to type the leading symbol (usually = or +) when entering formulas.

- There are several ways to enter data in a cell: pressing the RETURN key, pressing the ENTER key, or selecting another cell. Using the RETURN key both enters data and selects the cell below. Confusion can arise when students start typing without realizing that they are typing in a new cell.

- Students may forget to select a cell before they begin typing. They may end up typing something in the wrong cell, and changing the contents of that cell. If they have not yet entered the data, they can correct themselves. If they have entered the data, many applications have a command called "Undo Entry" that will bring back the previous entry in the cell.

- Students may forget to type cell references with the letter first, followed by the number. For instance, they may type 1A instead of A1.

- Students may use the letter **O** instead of zero, and the capital letter **I** or the small letter **l** instead of the number **1**.

I asked my students to write about how they identified the important informa- tion in the presentation. Kim and Janelle wrote, "We read it and wrote down the most important things. Most of the numbers are probably important. We also wrote down if the numbers are increasing or decreasing." □

We went further than taking a class survey of student responses for the question of what price one would pay for a custom T-shirt. With permission of the other teachers in my school, I sent out teams of four students to each classroom to survey students in other classes. □

How Many Sales at Tee-Time?

Have students review the phase overview on pages 20–21 in the Student Guide.

student page

1 Predicting How Price Will Affect Sales

Ask a student volunteer to give the business pre- sentation to the class from the Tee-Time T-Shirt Company. The presentation discusses the com- pany's dilemma—new competition has moved in next door and threatens their profits. Before stu- dents write their predictions about how the price that Tee-Time charges might affect their sales, you might want to discuss the important information in the presentation.

Throughout this lesson and the next, students will have several opportunities to explore the relation- ship between price and sales and how that affects profit. In this lesson, students will be thinking about how price affects profit more intuitively. As they gather various information and use tools to explore that question, stu- dents can remember their original predictions and see how their thinking has changed.

2 Gathering Data About Prices Customers Would Pay

Take a class survey of students' responses to the question, "What prices would you pay for a cus- tom-printed T-shirt?" You could ask students to raise their hands if they would pay $12, and keep their hands raised for each subsequent price they would be willing to pay. When you call out a price that students think is too high, they can lower their hands. Take a count of how many hands are still up for each price, and record that on the table you have prepared on chart paper. Keep this table visible for students throughout this lesson and the next, so they can refer to it while working on their graphs and spreadsheets.

The survey helps to highlight the realism of the price investigation students are conducting for the Tee-Time T-Shirt Company. Many business owners and consultants begin their analysis of pricing with a mar- ket survey. Ideally, the survey should show that fewer and fewer people will buy the product as the price increases.

hot topics

- *Collecting Data*
- *Graphing on the Coordinate Plane*

I think the price Tee Time charges will affect their sales because people might not buy the shirts if not too exp...

Price	No. of people who would pay this price
	25
.00	24
.00	24
4.00	23
15.00	23
16.00	21
$17.00	21
$18.00	20
$19.00	17

7 How Many Sales at Tee-Time?

USING GRAPHS TO EXPLORE SALES

Tee-Time T-Shirt Company wants help in deciding what price customers would be willing to pay for its T-shirts.
A survey your class conducts will provide data that you can graph. You will explore the relationship between price and the number of people who would buy T-shirts.

How might the price of T-shirts affect sales?

Predict How Price Will Affect Sales

Does charging more for a product always mean you make more money? Think about the Tee-Time T-Shirt Company presentation. Write a prediction about how the price that Tee-Time charges might affect sales.

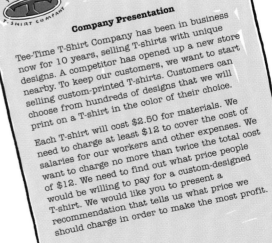

Company Presentation

Tee-Time T-Shirt Company has been in business now for 10 years, selling T-shirts with unique designs. A competitor has opened up a new store nearby. To keep our customers, we want to start selling custom-printed T-shirts. Customers can choose from hundreds of designs that we will print on a T-shirt in the color of their choice.

Each T-shirt will cost $2.50 for materials. We need to charge at least $12 to cover the cost of salaries for our workers and other expenses. We want to charge no more than twice the total cost of $12. We need to find out what price people would be willing to pay for a custom-designed T-shirt. We would like you to present a recommendation that tells us what price we should charge in order to make the most profit.

Since students surveyed more than 40 students, we had a discussion about how to graph the results. They noticed that some students wanted to pay the cheaper price when given the choice. However, when the students took the survey, they began with the higher price and went down as they took votes. When students were given only one opportunity to vote, some didn't realize just how low the prices would go! Therefore, many chose the in-between prices! □

My students tended to assume that there were invisible lines in between all the points that connected the points, dot to dot. So I focused on talking about why they assumed that and helping them think about scenarios where the "in-between" points, as we called them, did not fall on a line between two plotted points. They could then see that graphing fractional parts of people was silly. □

student page

3 Plotting Class Data on a Graph

Discuss the labeled axes and grid on the graph to help students locate the points to plot. As students complete Reproducible R19, Graphing Your Data, emphasize that they should plot the points but not connect them. In the next step, students will think about the relationships among the plotted points.

The horizontal axis of the graph shows a symbol for compressing the graph, to indicate that 0–11 have been omitted. If students are unfamiliar with this symbol, point it out to them. If students understand graphs and how to label the axes, you could give them Centimeter Grid Paper (R20) and have them construct their own graphs.

4 Discussing In-Between Points on the Graph

As you discuss the possible meanings of in-between points on the graph, make sure students recognize that the plotted points form a pattern. This pattern provides useful, general information about the relationship between the quantities on the axes. In Lesson 9, students will explore that idea further when they create and interpret line graphs.

- Could you plot additional points between the points already on the graph?

- Where do you think a point for a price of $15.50 would go? Would the number of people who would pay $15.50 be exactly between the number who would pay $15 and the number who would pay $16?

- Choose two prices where the number bought decreases. How many people do you think would buy at the price in between? Why?

student page

5 Analyzing Your Graph

After students have used their graphs to explore how price affects profit, you might want them to share their thinking with the class.

This writing assignment will help students realize that there are two effects of a price increase, and that these affect profits in opposite ways. If price goes up, you get more money for each item you sell, which tends to increase profits. However, you'll probably sell fewer items, which tends to decrease profits. It's hard to tell which effect "wins" without making the calculations. This is what students will be doing in the next lesson, using spreadsheets.

what to look for

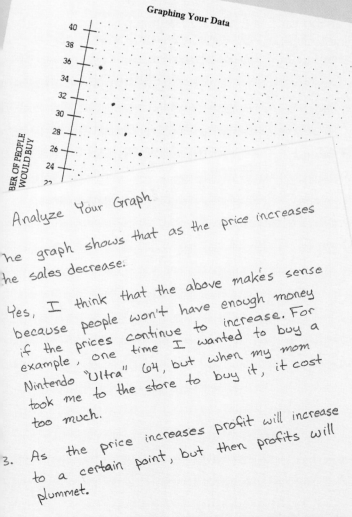

Graphing Your Data

NUMBER OF PEOPLE WOULD BUY

40
38
36
34
32
30
28
26
24
22

Analyze Your Graph

The graph shows that as the price increases the sales decrease.

Yes, I think that the above makes sense because people won't have enough money if the prices continue to increase. For example, one time I wanted to buy a Nintendo "Ultra" 64, but when my mom took me to the store to buy it, it cost too much.

3. As the price increases profit will increase to a certain point, but then profits will plummet.

Plot Class Data on a Graph

After your class has conducted a survey on what price people would pay for a T-shirt, set up your own graph showing the class data.

- Set up the graph to show the number of students who said they would buy a T-shirt at each priced listed in the survey.

- Plot the points on your graph. Do not draw lines that connect the points.

- Give your graph a title.

Analyze Your Graph

Think about how you could use your graph to explore the relationship between price and the number of people who will buy the product. Answer these questions.

- What trend does the graph show about sales and price?

- Does this correspond to what you know about the number of people who buy an item when its price increases? Explain your thinking.

- What do you think could happen to profit as the price increases?

How can you make a graph that shows the price people would pay for the product?

hot **words** | price
scatter plot

Homework
 page 42

GETTING DOWN TO BUSINESS   LESSON 7
© Creative Publications • MathScape   **23**

How Much Profit at Tee-Time?

Relating Graphs and Spreadsheets

Students had little trouble setting up the spreadsheets for the spreadsheet investigation. Some worked more quickly than others and got to use the spreadsheets first. Since we used more than 40 people in our survey, they needed to estimate how many students to include in each price category. This made students uncomfortable at first, but after some discussion, they were able to do it. □

Some students finished their spreadsheets more quickly than others, so I asked them to help their classmates. This worked well. The student helpers handled a lot of simple questions for me, and it was a nice opportunity for students to help one another. □

1 Designing a Spreadsheet

Discuss with the class the information that students should include in their spreadsheets. The total expenses are fixed at $100 for shirts to simplify the graphs in Step 3. Ask students to design their spreadsheets on paper first, reminding them that this will help organize their information for the computer. As they build their spreadsheets on the computer, point out that they might notice negative numbers for profits (depending on the class survey results).

This is the second time that students have set up a spreadsheet, so they are intentionally given less structure than in Lesson 6. Students are responsible for organizing the given information and entering the necessary numbers and formulas. If they are having difficulty, you could suggest these column headings: *Price, Sales* (number sold at that price), *Income, Expenses,* and *Profit. Price* and *Sales* come from the class data. *Expenses* are fixed at $100. As an extension, *Expenses* could be $2.50 per shirt times *Number of Shirts Sold,* but the graphs will not look as simple.

2 Using a Spreadsheet to Find the Best Price

student page

Provide computer time for students to use their spreadsheets to gather data and write a letter to Tee-Time recommending the best price.

Students waiting to use the computer, or who have finished on the computer, can work on Reproducible R21, Tee-Time's Profits. This reproducible is helpful but not essential. Students use the $P = I - E$ equation to figure out the net change in profit for each month and relate this information to the graph. Relating all three elements of the *PIE* relationship to a graph prepares students for Lesson 9. If they need help, suggest that they first decide whether profit is increasing, decreasing, or staying the same. Then they can refer to the numbers for income and expenses to figure out how much profit changes. See Assessment page A26 for more information.

If students want to test prices that weren't on the original class table, they can make their own estimates of how many shirts would be bought at those prices. Encourage them to keep the prices reasonable. After the discussion in Lesson 7, they should be more capable of making good estimates.

LESSON HOMEWORK

Getting Down to Business
Student Guide page 43
Solutions: Assessment page A36

hot topics

- Integer Operations
- Graphing on the Coordinate Plane

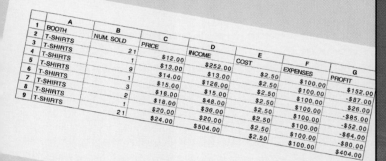

A	B	C	D	E	F	G
BOOTH	NUM. SOLD	PRICE	INCOME	COST	EXPENSES	PROFIT
T-SHIRTS						
T-SHIRTS	21	$12.00	$252.00			
T-SHIRTS	1	$13.00	$13.00	$2.50	$100.00	$152.00
T-SHIRTS	9	$14.00	$126.00	$2.50	$100.00	-$87.00
T-SHIRTS	1	$15.00	$15.00	$2.50	$100.00	$26.00
T-SHIRTS	3	$16.00	$48.00	$2.50	$100.00	-$85.00
T-SHIRTS	2	$18.00	$36.00	$2.50	$100.00	-$52.00
T-SHIRTS	1	$20.00	$20.00	$2.50	$100.00	-$64.00
	21	$24.00	$504.00	$2.50	$100.00	-$80.00
						$404.00

---

8 How Much Profit at Tee-Time?

What do you think is the best price for Tee-Time to charge for T-shirts? As you continue to investigate this question, you will explore spreadsheets and their related graphs. This will help you to better understand the relationships among price, income, and expenses.

Use a Spreadsheet to Find the Best Price

How can you use your spreadsheet to find a closer estimate for the best price?

Create your spreadsheet on the computer. Use it to test out different prices to find the highest profit. Make sure you do the following:

1 Keep track of the different prices you try, the number of sales, and the amount of profit at each price.

2 When you have decided on the best price to charge, write your recommendation letter to Tee-Time. Include a clear explanation of the price that will result in the most profit and how your information led you to make this recommendation.

3 Make a copy of your spreadsheet with the best price highlighted. Attach it to your letter.

Information to Include in Your Spreadsheet

- different possible prices (from the class survey)

- number of sales at each different price (from the class survey)

- income at each price

- expenses (Base this on 40 shirts at a cost to us of $2.50 per shirt. Figure on $100 for expenses at whatever price we charge.)

- the profit at each price

Graphs were easy for my students because they had graphed before. The only graph they had trouble with was the one for profit and graphing negative numbers. Still, quite a few good graphs were produced. One student commented that the graphs gave a good picture of what happened. They were interested in the graph for expenses, since it was a straight line! □

The discussion of the graphs helped to summarize what most students had observed—when income went up, their profit went up. Students also observed that when they had consistent expenses, they needed to generate some sales to get a profit! □

student page

3 Making Graphs from Spreadsheets

Before students make graphs from their spreadsheets, you might want to show the class a sample graph like the one on the next page. Remind students to use a consistent scale for the numbers on the axis, and suggest that they include negative numbers because profits may fall below the break-even point at some prices.

These graphs deepen students' understanding of the effect of price changes on each aspect of the relationships among profit, income, and expenses. The graphs also lay the groundwork for the next lesson, in which students will interpret and create qualitative line graphs that emphasize the relationships among profits, income, and expenses. In that lesson, students will encounter some graphs in which the profits fall below zero.

student page

4 Analyzing Your Graphs

After students have analyzed their own graphs, ask a few students to draw their graphs on the board, so that there is at least one example of a graph for income, expenses, and profit. Have a class discussion about these graphs and how they show the relationship between price and profit.

This activity emphasizes to students how income and expenses interact to determine profits. In the next lesson, students will examine similar graphs that contain just the shapes formed by the points. They'll be asked to describe the relationships among profit, income, and expenses without using numbers. The specific shape of the graphs that students create will depend on the class data, and may vary from student to student if they have chosen to track some additional prices. All of the expense graphs, however, should show points falling in a horizontal line because expenses remain fixed at $100. Since expenses are fixed, there should be a strong correlation among the shapes of the graphs for profits and income.

DO STUDENTS HAVE:

- *a spreadsheet that includes the necessary information to find out the highest profit?*
- *a letter with a clear explanation of the price that will result in the greatest profit?*
- *graphs that show relationships between price and income, price and expenses, and price and profit?*

See *Getting Down to Business* Assessment page A13 for assessment information.

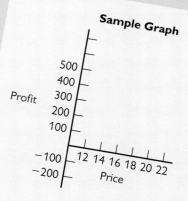

Sample Graph

Profit / Price

Make Graphs from Spreadsheets

Graphs will help Tee-Time see how profit, income, and expenses are related. Use the data from your spreadsheet to plot points on three separate graphs:

1 Create a graph showing price versus income.

2 Create a graph showing price versus expenses.

3 Create a graph showing price versus profit.

Attach these three graphs to your recommendation letter and spreadsheet.

How can you show the relationships among price, income, and expenses on a graph?

Analyze Your Graphs

To analyze the relationship between price and profit, use the three graphs that you made to write answers to these questions:

- How would you describe the shape formed by the points in each of your three graphs? Do the graphs form straight lines? Do they change directions? At what points? Why?

- What does the shape of the graph tell you about the relationship between price and income? price and expenses? price and profit?

- If you compare all three graphs, what can you learn about income, expenses, and profit?

- Does the profit graph ever fall below zero? At what point? Why?

- From the information on the graph, what do you think would be the most profitable price for Tee-Time to charge? Why?

hot **words** | spreadsheet
profit

Homework

page 43

GETTING DOWN TO BUSINESS LESSON 8
© Creative Publications • MathScape **25**

Creating and Interpreting Qualitative Graphs

This was a new type of graph for students because they were used to specific numbers that they needed to graph on the vertical axis. I showed them a rough outline of the graph given in the lesson. Students finally made variations of this graph, but still had trouble deciding how to fill it in. Several had difficulty interpreting the information given, but worked most of it out in their heterogeneous groups! Comments I heard were:

- *"We all had the same months, and we all put time on the bottom."*

- *"This is the highest point because this is where they made the biggest profit."* □

Months Later at Tee-Time

1 Making Qualitative Graphs

After students have read through the information from the Tee-Time T-Shirt Company, talk with the class about different ways to set up a graph. One way is to fill in general descriptions on the *y*-axis, as shown in the graph below, and another way is to use sample profit numbers. Then ask students to make their own graphs.

👆 Make sure students include all of the information provided in the information from Tee-Time. The purpose of creating this graph is to help students move from quantitative graphs with specific, numerical data points to qualitative graphs that show the general pattern in the data. See Assessment page A27 for answers.

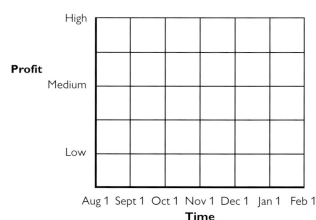

2 Comparing the Graphs

In small groups, have students compare the graphs they created. Use questions such as these to foster group discussions or to discuss together as a class.

- In what ways are your graphs similar? different?

- What can you tell about profit over time from the similarities in people's graphs?

- What is the highest point on your graph? Tell why you think that is the highest point.

- What do you think was the most profitable month for Tee-Time? Why?

👆 As students discuss the similarities and differences, listen to determine if they are not only noticing that there are various ways to graph the same information, but also that the similarities in the general shapes of the graphs give some important information about profit. This helps students focus more on the overall shapes of the graphs.

hot topics

- *Displaying Data*
- *Analyzing Data*

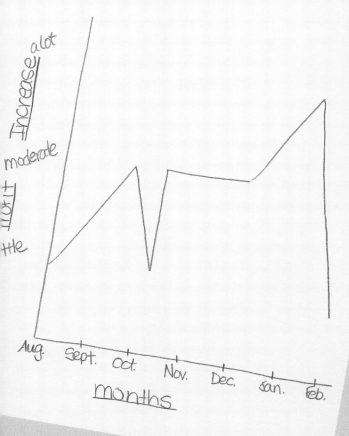

9 Months Later at Tee-Time

CREATING AND
INTERPRETING
QUALITATIVE
GRAPHS

Businesses often try to predict trends that will affect their profits. Graphs that have no numbers can be a useful way of showing general trends. As you create and interpret these kinds of graphs, you will see relationships among profit, income, and expenses in a new way.

Make Qualitative Graphs

How could you make a graph without numbers?

Tee-Time T-Shirt Company wants your help in preparing graphs to present to their board of directors. They don't want the board to look at lots of numbers. They want these graphs to show general trends in the business over the past 6 months. Use the information in the Tee-Time T-Shirt Company Semi-Annual Report to make a graph of their profit without numbers.

Semi-Annual Report

Aug. 1 We introduce our new custom designed T-shirts. We are the only T-shirt company selling them, so our sales increase quite a lot. Our expenses rise only a little. Sales keep increasing until Sept. 15.

Sept. 16 We decide to hire a local celebrity, Arnold Quartzdigger, to do our TV commercials for us. Mr. Quartzdigger asks for a high salary, so our expenses increase quite a bit. On Oct. 2, we ask him to leave because he is too expensive.

Oct. 3 We learn that our competitor, Weekend Wear Clothing, has started selling custom designed T-shirts, and is selling them for less. We find a supplier

that will sell us T-shirts and designs for less than we were paying. We lower our price below Weekend Wear's. Our income drops a little, but our expenses also drop by about the same amount.

Nov. 15 We have expanded our line of custom designed T-shirts to include six new colors that Weekend Wear does not have. Our sales increase gradually until Dec. 1 while our expenses stay the same.

Dec. 1 Many people are buying gifts for the holidays, so we lower our prices slightly to encourage more people to buy from us. It works! Our sales keep going up throughout the month of December, while our expenses stay about the same.

Jan. 5 The holidays are over, and people are not spending as much money. This month we don't sell many T-shirts, even though our expenses remain about the same.

GETTING DOWN TO BUSINESS LESSON 9
26 © Creative Publications • MathScape

As I walked around the class, we talked about the story that the graphs tell. This made it easier to fill in the missing graph. Some of my students were still reluctant to create a graph without numbers. They insisted on some kind of measure for the vertical axis, so I encouraged them to use words, such as "low/medium/high" or "least profit/some profit/most profit." □

Felicity developed a strategy for analyzing the graphs that worked for a number of classmates as well. She drew the income and expense lines on the same graph. "That way, it's easy to see when they're close together or crossing and when they are far apart." □

I gave students the choice of working in groups or alone to make a poster presentation. I also gave them a choice of making a large poster or making an individual, smaller poster for their presentation. Most of the students used graphs similar to the ones in Lesson 8 for their presentations. □

student page

3 Creating the Missing Graphs

Ask students to read through the memo from the Tee-Time T-Shirt Company before distributing the Missing Graphs reproducible to students. These qualitative graphs show general trends for income, expenses, and profit from the past seven months at Tee-Time. To help students get started, you may want to walk the class through the first problem. For the first four problems, encourage students to compare the shape, angle, and placement of the income and expense graphs in order to make determinations about the profit graph. See Assessment page A27 for answers.

☝ Working with qualitative graphs encourages students to think about the relationships among profit, income, and expenses in a more abstract way. They learn to draw general conclusions about the relationships, such as, "When income increases and expenses remain constant, profit will also increase." The analysis of these qualitative graphs is very similar to the analysis students did of the quantitative graphs at the end of Lesson 8. The main difference between those graphs and these (besides the absence of numbers) is that the earlier graphs measured price on the horizontal axis, while these measure time. However, the relationships among the shapes of the income, expense, and profit graphs are the same.

student page

4 Describing Income, Expenses, and Profit

Before students create posters describing how income, expenses, and profit are related in the graphs, you may want to choose two or three sets of graphs from Missing Graphs for students to use on their posters. Another option is to let students choose the ones they would like. This poster serves as assessment for the phase.

☝ At the end of this phase, you might want to revisit the chart of business terms started in Lesson 1. Students will be better able to revise their definitions of some of the words, using what they have learned in this phase. They may want to add new words and definitions from this phase to the chart.

DO STUDENTS' POSTERS INCLUDE:

- *two or three sets of graphs?*
- *explanations of each graph?*
- *an explanation of the relationships among the three graphs that shows an understanding of the relationships among profit, income, and expenses?*

See *Getting Down to Business* Assessment pages A14–A15 for assessment information.

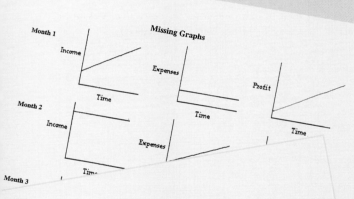

Create the Missing Graphs

The handout Missing Graphs is a collection of graphs showing general trends for the Tee-Time T-Shirt Company. The graphs show increases and decreases in income, expenses, and profit during the last seven months. Use the information from each pair of graphs to sketch the missing third graph. Be sure to label the new graph you sketch and give it a title.

> **Given two out of three graphs, how could you create the third graph?**

Describe Income, Expenses, and Profit

Read the memo below from the manager of Enterprise Consultants, Inc. Provide the information the manager needs for the presentation to Tee-Time T-Shirt Company.

To: Employees of Enterprise Consultants, Inc.

You have done an excellent job interpreting the information from Tee-Time. I am now preparing to give a presentation to Tee-Time to teach them more about profit, income, and expenses. I would like to have some posters to help me explain concepts clearly to Tee-Time's employees.

Here is what I'd like you to do:

1. Create a poster with two or three sets of profit, income, and expense graphs.

2. Explain in writing what each graph shows.

3. Explain in writing how the income and expense graphs result in the profit graph.

hot **words** | qualitative graphs
trend

Homework

page 44

GETTING DOWN TO BUSINESS LESSON 9
© Creative Publications • MathScape **27**

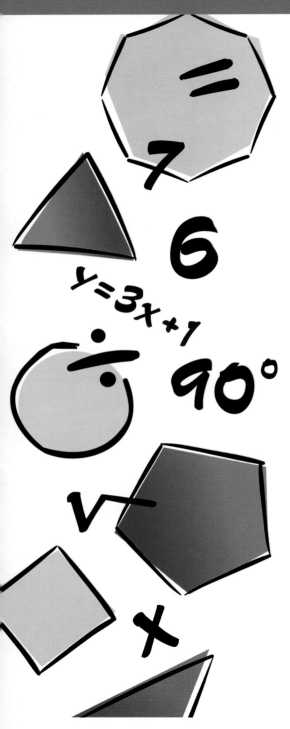

A TEACHER REFLECTS

Since most of my students were feeling pretty confident about spreadsheets and their ability to use them on the computer, more of their questions in this phase were related to graphs. We talked about the in-between points on the graph because most of the students had a difficult time understanding this. I think it was because most of the graphing they had done in the past had been where they had connected the dots. So I decided to throw in a little discussion of discrete mathematics, which is really what this was, to show the difference between discrete and continuous relationships. I hoped this would help students learn how to *know* when to connect the dots. Here are some of the examples I gave the class:

Continuous	Discrete
snake crawling	rabbit hopping
dimmer light switch	on/off light switch
rolling a ball	bouncing a ball
running water	ice cubes

I pointed out that in Lesson 7, connecting the points indicates that there are fractions of people in-between. We had a lively and humorous discussion about this, as we laughed about having "$\frac{1}{3}$ of a person," but in the end I felt like students came away with a greater understanding of *why* we asked them not to connect the dots. This felt much better than simply telling them not to connect the dots.

The idea of graphs without numbers was new to my students. They wanted exact numbers. We brainstormed as a class other examples of graphs without numbers. Ideas students had were graphing test scores as high, medium, and low; graphing population growth as fast, moderate, and slow; and graphing the number of students who played sports as many, some, and none. Once they seemed to get over this "psychological" barrier, they were much more comfortable with the idea.

When students shared their posters at the end of this phase, it was obvious to me that they not only understood how to create graphs to show income, expenses, and profit, but that they had clearly learned much about the relationships between profit, income, and expenses. Some of the parents were stopping by to comment on what their children were doing with this unit. "I'm glad to see the realism and the concept of profit/loss being investigated." "This is what I do in my business and to be able to help my daughter understand what she is doing is great."

PHASE FOUR

A Case Study of North Mall Cinema

After organizing the information from North Mall Cinema, students build spreadsheets from scratch and make recommendations to North Mall Cinema for improving profit.

LESSON 10

North Mall Cinema's Project

The unit's final project, which can also serve as a phase assessment, is a case study that develops throughout the last three lessons. As consultants to North Mall Cinema, students become familiar in this lesson with the requirements of the project and organize the information from the cinema. After brainstorming a list of possible what-if questions to explore, students limit their list to those that will yield the best profits for the cinema.

Mathematical Goals

- Pose what-if questions to explore on the spreadsheet.

- Apply understanding of the Profit = Income − Expenses relationship in order to select what-if questions that will result in increased profit.

- Organize data on income and expenses, and calculate totals for both categories.

MATERIALS

PER STUDENT

- Reproducible R23

PREPARATION

Before beginning this lesson, plan the project so that it fits your students. See North Mall Cinema, Reproducible R23, and the note on page 68 to help you organize the project.

Students should work in pairs to brainstorm ideas and to provide feedback on each others' work. However, they should produce their own individual work.

LESSON 11

North Mall Cinema's Spreadsheet

In this lesson, students continue their case study as they apply and extend what they have learned in the unit about the Profit = Income − Expenses relationship on a spreadsheet. They design their spreadsheet from scratch on paper and then build it on the computer. Using the spreadsheet as a tool to explore the what-if questions they generated in the preceding lesson enables students to find ways to increase profit.

Mathematical Goals

- Organize information into a spreadsheet.

- Use the spreadsheet as a tool to explore what-if questions about increasing profit.

- Apply and extend understanding of the Profit = Income − Expenses relationship.

MATERIALS

PER STUDENT

- Reproducible R24 (optional)

PREPARATION

Students will need access to computers that have a spreadsheet program. See page vii. Students will need the what-if questions they wrote in Lesson 10. Students should work in pairs to brainstorm ideas and to provide feedback on each others' work, but they should produce their own individual work.

LESSON 12

North Mall Cinema's Report

Creating a report for North Mall Cinema that contains recommendations for improving profit is the focus of this lesson. After students write their reports, they exchange them with their partners and provide feedback on each other's work. They make revisions based on their partners' suggestions. In this final lesson, students apply and extend what they have learned in the unit about posing what-if questions, making recommendations from data, and describing the relationships among profit, income, and expenses.

PREPARATION

Students will need their three what-if questions from Lesson 10 and the spreadsheets they created in Lesson 11. Students should work in pairs to brainstorm ideas and to provide feedback on each other's work, but they should produce their own work.

Mathematical Goals

- Make recommendations based on data from the spreadsheet investigation.

- Describe the relationship between profit, income, and expenses.

TECHNOLOGY OPTIONS

Checking or Collecting Student Work Done on the Spreadsheet

If students can print out their spreadsheets, any cell that contains a formula will show the result of that formula, not the formula itself. So you may want to ask students to print two copies of their spreadsheet: one that shows the results they had on the screen, and another copy that shows their underlying formulas. Most spreadsheet applications have a command to show the underlying formula. In Excel or ClarisWorks, the "Show Formula" command is found under the Options menu. Within this menu, select Display and click in the box that says Formula. Other applications may have a simular command.

If students can't print out their spreadsheets, there are several ways you can collect students' work.

- Give them a disk, and have them save their spreadsheet in a file on that disk. Collect the disks.

- Have students save their spreadsheets in a file on their computers' hard drive. You will then need to look at their files on each computer. Make sure there is space on the hard drive for students to save their work.

- Students can copy down their spreadsheets on paper templates.

Involving a Computer Teacher

As students continue working with spreadsheets in this phase, you may decide to enlist the help of the computer teacher in your school. The computer teacher can help by:

- Offering additional instruction and/or support regarding the mechanics of using spreadsheets. Examples are: how to change the size of a column, how to make a dollar sign ($) appear automatically in a cell, and how to change the font size.

- Using computer class time to give students extra practice in using a spreadsheet.

- Using computer class time to give students time to work on assignments from the unit that use a spreadsheet.

	A	B	C	D
	#adults	adult price	# of children	children price
1	475	$6.00	100	$4.00
2	600	$6.00	175	$4.00
3	475	$6.00	100	$4.00
4	475	$8.00	100	$5.00
5				
6	adult income	children income	income per theater	total income
7	=A2*B2	=C2*D2	=A8+B8	=C8*4
8	=A3*B3	=C3*D3	=A9+B9	=C9*4
9	=A4*B4	=C4*D4	=A10+B10	=C10*4
10	=A5*B5	=C5*D5	=A11+B11	=C11*4
11				
12				total salary	sal
13	# of employees	# of hours	wage	
14	20	8	$7.00	=A15*B15*C15
15	20	8	$7.00	=A16*B16*C16
16	20	8	$7.00	=A17*B17*C17
17	20	8	$7.00	=A18*B18*C18
18				
19	movie rental per theater	total rental	building cost per theater	total cost
20	$1000.00	=A22*4	=D22/4	$1800.00
21	$1000.00	=A23*4	=D23/4	$1800.00
22	$500.00	=A24*4	=D24/4	$1800.0
23	$1000.00	=A25*4	=D25/4	$1800.0
24				
25			profit	
26	total expenses	=D15+B22+D22	=D8-A28	
27	=D16+B23+D23	=D9-A29		
28	=D10-A30			

Common Spreadsheet Command Shortcuts

There are many features of spreadsheets that provide shortcuts for common commands. Of those, there are two that students with spreadsheet experience may already know and find useful. These are not required in the lessons in this unit, but you may choose to teach them to your class.

The "sum" function is a shortcut for adding several numbers. Type =sum(first cell:last cell). For example, in the spreadsheet shown, the number 700 in cell B6 could also be found using the formula =sum(B2:B4).

The "fill down" command copies the contents of a cell into all the selected cells beneath it. For example, in the spreadsheet shown, the cell D2 has the formula =B2*C2.

	A	B	C	D
1		Number of Tickets	Price	Income
2	Movie 1	150	$7	=B2*C2
3	Movie 2	250	$7	
4	Movie 3	300	$7	
5				
6	Total	700		

By selecting cells D2, D3, and D4, and then choosing "fill down" from a menu, cell D3 will have the formula =B3*C3, and cell D4 will have =B4*C4. The spreadsheet automatically adjusts the cell row numbers to refer to the appropriate cells for each row.

	A	B	C	D
1		Number of Tickets	Price	Income
2	Movie 1	150	$7	=B2*C2
3	Movie 2	250	$7	=B3*C3
4	Movie 3	300	$7	=B4*C4
5				
6	Total	700		

The formula will appear in the cell while you are typing it in. Once you enter this information by pressing the RETURN key, the result of the formula will appear in the cell.

The command to "fill right" performs the same task horizontally.

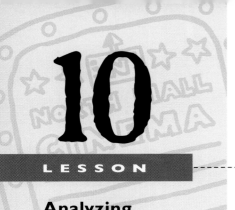

10

LESSON

Analyzing the Data

There was a lot of information for my students to organize. To get them started, I had students first circle the information they needed. Then I had them calculate the information for each theater for each day. It helped them to take the time to work through this step. □

To make the situation more realistic, I added the following about concession stands: "The movie theater buys candy bars, boxes of candy, soda, ice cream bars, and paper goods every week, costing around $4,000 each day. They have figured out that, on average, they sell $7,200 of concessions each day." Although this did make the project more complex, I felt like my students thrived on this extra challenge. □

North Mall Cinema's Project

Have students review the phase overview on pages 28–29 in the Student Guide.

student page

1 Discussing the Final Project

Distribute Reproducible R23, North Mall Cinema, to students. Ask them to read and then discuss the first part, North Mall Cinema Project Sequence. Encourage students to ask questions to ensure that they understand the scope of the project.

👆 The final project spans Lessons 10–12. This lesson covers the first three of the six steps of the project, as outlined in the North Mall Cinema Project Sequence. If your students have no experience with large projects, you could provide more opportunities for checking and revising work. If your students are experienced, you could let them help with the planning.

2 Organizing Information About North Mall Cinema

Ask students to read the reproducible's second part, Information About North Mall Cinema. Then have them list and calculate both income and expenses for each theater per day. Then have students list and calculate income and expenses for each theater per day.

👆 As students make lists, they are summarizing the information about income and expenses. Here is one way that income could be calculated for each theater per day: (475 adults × $6) + (100 children × $4) = $3,250. There are four theaters, so income for one day with average attendance would be $13,000. Here is one way that expenses could be calculated per day: (20 people × 8 hours × $7 per hour) + (4 movie rentals × $1,000) + $1,800 building costs = $6,920. Questions based on these calculations could help students if they are having difficulty getting started.

hot **topics**

- *Displaying Data*
- *If/Then Statements*

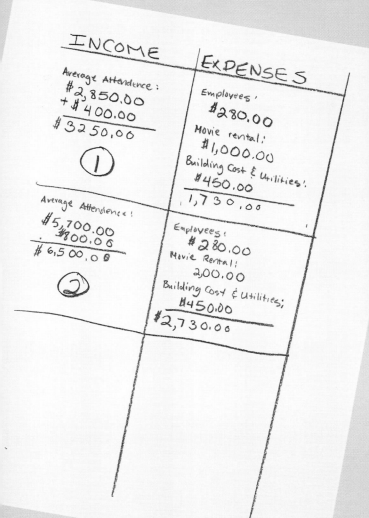

INCOME   EXPENSES

Average Attendance:
2,850.00
+ # 400.00
# 3,250.00

①

Employees:
280.00

Movie rental:
1,000.00

Building Cost & Utilities:
450.00

1,730.00

Average Attendance:
5,700.00
. # 800.00
6,500.00

②

Employees:
280.00

Movie Rental:
200.00

Building Cost & Utilities:
450.00

2,730.00

---

10 North Mall
Cinema's Project

**ANALYZING
THE DATA**

As a final project, you will act as a consultant to a business. Your job will be to research how North Mall Cinema can increase their profits. The first two steps in the project are organizing information about the business and listing what-if questions to explore.

Organize Information About North Mall Cinema

How could you determine the income and expenses for each theater per day?

Read the memo from North Mall Cinema outlining your final project and the second part of the handout North Mall Cinema, entitled Information About North Mall Cinema. To complete Step 1 of your final project, do this:

- Make a list of income and expenses for each theater per day.

- Calculate income and expenses for each theater per day. Show your work.

You will also complete Step 2 of your final project in this lesson, followed by Steps 3 and 4 in Lesson 11, and Step 5 in Lesson 12.

To: Consultants of
Enterprise Consultants, Inc.

We at North Mall Cinema are pleased that you will be working with us to help us increase our profits. We hope to make a total profit of at least $10,000 per day. See the Information About North Mall Cinema we have provided. Use it to complete these steps and make your recommendation.

Step 1. Organize data provided about North Mall Cinema.

Step 2. List what-if questions to explore.

Step 3. Design a spreadsheet.

Step 4. Investigate profit on the spreadsheet.

Step 5. Create a report on improving profit.

As I walked around the room, I noticed that in their enthusiasm some students were coming up with questions that were quite realistic but would be hard to show on a spreadsheet. I encouraged all questions that showed thought, but reminded students that they were going to work with these questions later, so they should be sure that at least some of their questions were easy to experiment with on the spreadsheet. □

My students were unaccustomed to designing their own rubrics, so I planned to use the rubric as it was written. This step became a clarification of the assignment for students as they asked me specific questions and I asked them for examples of what each part meant. □

3 Listing What-If Questions to Explore

As pairs of students brainstorm what-if questions for their spreadsheets, remind them to think of questions that might help to make North Mall Cinema more profitable. You may want to review the three questions that students select to make sure they result in numerical data that can be tested on the spreadsheet. If they don't, encourage students to go back to their list of seven questions, or to brainstorm additional ones. Have students save these questions for Lessons 11 and 12.

Students may start to focus on nonmathematical details, such as suggesting better popcorn or nicer bathrooms. Help students rephrase some of these suggestions into what-if questions that focus on a numerical amount. For example, rather than "Show more popular movies," suggest, "What if the movie theater sold *more* tickets?" Identifying the questions they want to explore will help students think about how to design a spreadsheet to answer those questions.

4 Discussing the Project Assessment

After students have discussed the scope of the project and selected their what-if questions, they should understand the project well enough to think about the Assessment Rubric shown on pages A18–A19. You may want to display this on a chart or on the overhead projector. Save ample time to answer any questions students have on how they will be evaluated after the class has discussed the rubric.

It is essential that students understand in the beginning how their work will be evaluated. The Assessment Rubric may be used as is, or as a starting point for students to develop their own assessment criteria. Involving students in deciding on the quality criteria for assessing their projects gives them a sense of ownership and clarifies expectations.

what to look for

DO STUDENTS HAVE:
- *a list of income and expenses, and how they were calculated?*
- *seven what-if questions?*
- *three what-if questions that can be explored on spreadsheet?*

See *Getting Down to Business* Assessment page A17 for assessment information.

1. What if the building costs go down?
2. What if the employees only make $4.00 an h...
3. What if the price for adults were $10.00, an... children were $8.00?
4. What if when the first two... the people who came t... would double.
5. What i...

what-if questions to explore

...out, it

...at if movie rentals went up? ...00?
...at if more movie theaters were added?
...at if only one more theater opened?
...hat if the employees got a 50¢ raise?
...what if movie rental price went down?
...what if ½ the employees got fired?
...what if Adult tickets raised $1.00?

Brainstorm — bring more things

lose $ — gain $

add...

List What-If Questions to Explore

Think of suggestions that might make North Mall Cinema more profitable before you complete the tasks below. Brainstorming ideas with a partner might be helpful.

1 Use the suggestions to make a list of what-if questions to explore on the spreadsheet. List at least seven what-if questions.

2 From your list of what-if questions, select three questions that you feel would have the greatest impact on North Mall Cinema's profits and write them down.

> How can North Mall Cinema increase its profits, and what questions would you ask to find out?

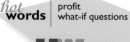
hot **words** | profit / what-if questions

Home**w**ork

page 45

GETTING DOWN TO BUSINESS LESSON 10
© Creative Publications • MathScape **31**

11

Exploring

What-If

Questions

Some students finished their spreadsheets more quickly than others, so I asked them to help their classmates. This worked well. The student helpers handled a lot of simple questions for me, and it was an opportunity for students to help one another. □

North Mall Cinema's Spreadsheet

1 Discussing Spreadsheet Organization

Make sure that students have the three what-if questions they wrote in the last lesson. Initiate a class discussion using questions such as those below to help students think about how to structure their spreadsheets to explore their three what-if questions.

- What are the income and expenses for North Mall Cinema?

- What information will you want in your spreadsheet to help you answer your what-if questions?

- How do you think this information should be organized?

2 Designing a Spreadsheet

student page

Before students design their spreadsheets on paper, tell them that they will be transferring their spreadsheets to the computer later in this lesson. You might want student volunteers to review some tips students discovered about spreadsheets—how to print in landscape mode, how to change the size of the column width, and how to double click on a cell to choose currency.

Since students have already created two spreadsheets, this spreadsheet assignment is the least structured in the unit. Most students should be able to set up a spreadsheet with relatively little guidance—deciding what information to include, organizing this information, and inputting the appropriate data and formulas. Because students are working in pairs, they can discuss different ideas with each other if they are having difficulty with some aspect of their design. Encourage each member of the pair to construct an individual design, however. Students will create their spreadsheets on the computer in Step 4.

LESSON HOMEWORK

Getting Down to Business
Student Guide page 46
Solutions: Assessment page A39

hot **topics**

- *Size and Scale*
- *Spreadsheets*

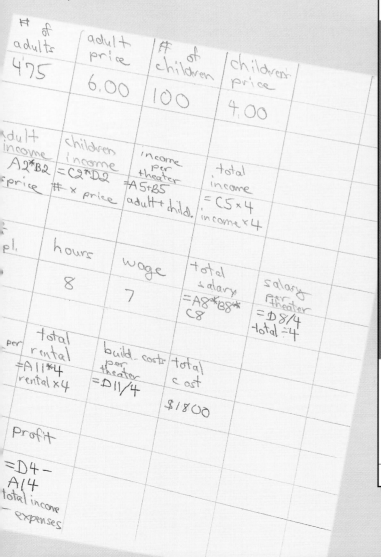

Handwritten spreadsheet notes:

# of adults	adult price	# of children	children's price
4'75	6.00	100	4.00

adult income	children income	income per theater	total income
A2*B2	=C2*D2	=A5+B5	=C5×4
price #×price	#×price	adult+child.	income×4

pl.	hours	wage	total salary	salary per theater
	8	7	=A8*B8* C8	=D8/4 total ÷4

per rental	build costs per theater	total cost
=A11*4 rental×4	=D11/4	$1800

profit
=D4 - A14 total income - expenses

11

North Mall Cinema's Spreadsheet

EXPLORING WHAT-IF QUESTIONS

What spreadsheet can you create to help you decide how to increase North Mall Cinema's profits? To complete the third and fourth steps of the project, you will design a spreadsheet on the computer and use it to explore the what-if questions you came up with in the last lesson.

Design a Spreadsheet

How could you design a spreadsheet showing information about North Mall Cinema?

Design your own spreadsheet. Use the second part of the handout North Mall Cinema, entitled Information About North Mall Cinema. Create the spreadsheet on paper first. You will be using the spreadsheet you create on paper to build a spreadsheet on the computer later on.

- Be sure your spreadsheet calculates the total income, the total expenses, and the profit for each of the four theaters at the North Mall Cinema.

- As you design your spreadsheet, you might want to discuss ideas with your partner.

GETTING DOWN TO BUSINESS LESSON 11
32 © Creative Publications • MathScape

I was surprised by the questions my students were asking as they worked on Part 1 of Predicting Profits. They seemed to be very conscious of the complexity of a business transaction or event. For example, for Question 2, one of my students decided that expenses would go up due to renovation costs, and that income would go down because a theater would have to close for these renovations. As a result of these renovations, income would increase, but expenses would also increase because the theater would need to hire more employees to handle the increase in customers. □

I checked students' designs before they created their spreadsheets on the computer, but I wanted to make sure their spreadsheets were on the right track so they would get good information to write recommendations. I went around to each machine with a disk and asked students to save their spreadsheets on my disk. Later I printed all of the spreadsheets with the formulas showing. □

3 Reviewing the Spreadsheet Designs

Before students proceed with the investigation, be sure to review their spreadsheet designs and check that the items shown below have been included. You could have partners check each other's spreadsheets to make sure all of the items are included.

Items to Include in the Spreadsheet

1. Ticket prices as part of income
2. Total income for each movie
3. Salaries, rental fees, and building/utility costs as part of expenses
4. Total expenses for each movie
5. Total profit
6. Rows or columns for each movie
7. Formulas to calculate income, expenses, and profit
8. Accurate spreadsheet notation

It is important that students have ample time to revise their spreadsheet designs if necessary and add any items that have been left out. This will save time once students get their turns on the computer and will help ensure that they will use their spreadsheets effectively to explore different ways of increasing profit for North Mall Cinema.

4 Investigating Profit on the Spreadsheet

student page

Using their spreadsheet designs on paper as a guide, students should now build their spreadsheets on the computer and explore the three what-if questions they chose in Lesson 10. Make sure they save their spreadsheets to use in the next lesson.

Students waiting to use the computer, or who have finished, could work on the reproducible Predicting Profits. This helps them relate what-if questions to statements about income and expenses and to qualitative graphs about profit. As students work on Part 1 of Predicting Profits, Reproducible R24, encourage them to think about the effect that any business transaction would have on both income and expenses. Predicting Profits is helpful but not essential. See Assessment page A28 for more information.

If you do not have one computer for each student, you may want to have students work at the computer in pairs. As one student makes entries on his or her spreadsheet, the other can record the results on paper.

what to look for

DO STUDENTS' SPREADSHEET DESIGNS AND INVESTIGATIONS INCLUDE:

- *a well-organized spreadsheet with all the necessary information?*
- *formulas written in correct spreadsheet notation and included in appropriate columns?*
- *what-if questions that can be explored on the spreadsheet?*
- *a clear, well-organized record of results from investigating each question?*
- *an explanation of how changes in income and expenses affect profit?*

See *Getting Down to Business* Assessment page A17 for assessment information.

Investigate Profit on the Spreadsheet

Using the spreadsheet you designed on paper, build your spreadsheet on the computer. Then use it to explore each of the three what-if questions you wrote in the last lesson. For each question you explore, write the following information:

- the question you are exploring
- what you tried on the spreadsheet
- whether it helped you reach North Mall Cinema's goal of making at least $10,000 profit each day
- whether you increased or decreased income or expenses

> **How can you use a spreadsheet to explore your what-if questions?**

hot **words** | spreadsheet formula

page 46

Making Profit Recommendations

North Mall Cinema's Report

Students liked brainstorming ideas and occasionally defended their own ideas boisterously, pointing to their spreadsheets to show that their idea worked. □

By this time, most students felt well prepared to begin this assignment and were anxious to get started. They understood the PIE relationship, and the reports were completed in less time than I had anticipated. □

1 Brainstorming Recommendations

Make sure students have their spreadsheets from Lesson 11. Ask them to review their own and their partner's spreadsheets. Then suggest that they use both spreadsheets to brainstorm one, two, or three recommendations for improving profit.

The purpose of brainstorming ideas is to prepare students for the report they will write in this lesson. Emphasize the importance of basing their recommendations on the data in the spreadsheets, rather than on guesses or intuitions.

student page

2 Creating a Report on Improving Profit

Ask students to write a report to North Mall Cinema with their final recommendation(s) for improving profit. Remind them to consider what they have learned in the unit about the Profit = Income − Expenses relationship.

homework options

LESSON HOMEWORK

Getting Down to Business
Student Guide page 47
Solutions: Assessment page A40

hot topics

- *Analyzing Data*
- *Square and Cube Roots*

Brainstorming

1. Get more people to come to the shows.
2. Reduce building expenses and raise prices.
3. Reduce all expenses and increase atte...

Report on Increasing Profit

...r carefully studyhing North Mall Cinema's income and expenses, I
...eve either of the following recommendations would increase profit to
...,000 per day.

...Increase attendance at the theaters. The theaters hold 300 people each.
...each of them have four showtimes, you could have 1200 people in each
...eater each day. Instead you have 575. Increasing adult attendance to
...00 and child attendance to 175 would give you a profit of $10,280 per day.
...his would increase your income while not effecting your expenses.
Therefore your profit would increase.

2. You could also raiser profits to at least $10,000 a day by a combining
raising prices and lowering movie rental expenses. Raise the price to $7.50
per adult and $4.50 for children. Find a company to rent movies more
cheaply or show movies that are cheaper to rent. If you can pay $750
instead of $1,000 per movie your profit will be $10,130 pwe day. This
would increase your income by increasing the price. Renting cheaper
movies would decrease your expenses. Increasing income and lowering
expenses both increase profit.

3. Another way to increase your profit is to increase both attendance and
the price while reducing expenses at the same time. Our spreadsheet
shows that if you had 550 adults and 125 children at the show and raised
the adult price to $6.25 you would increase income to $15,750. Then you
could reduce your employee number to 16, eliminating one employee per
showing, rent movies that cost only $800 and decrease maintenance costs
...o $1400. This would result in a daily profit of $10,254. In this example, you
...income while reducing all expenses and therefore increase

---

12 North Mall Cinema's Report

MAKING PROFIT
RECOMMENDATIONS

The feedback of a partner can be helpful in refining your work. After writing a report for your final project, you will have a chance to revise it and make improvements based on your partner's feedback. You will want your report to look as professional as possible.

How would you write a report that gives recommendations for improving profit?

Create a Report on Improving Profit

Write a report to North Mall Cinema. Include the following in your report:

- a description of one, two, or three recommendations for meeting North Mall Cinema's profit goal of at least $10,000 per day

- an explanation of each recommendation

- how your recommendation(s) are related to profit, income, and expenses

Attach to your report the what-if questions you explored, the spreadsheet you designed, and the information you got from your spreadsheet.

 GETTING DOWN TO BUSINESS   LESSON 12

My students were very positive in their reaction to each other's reports. It was difficult for them to understand that while being positive was important, constructive feedback from others could focus on areas that needed improvement. Their comments tended to focus on spelling and grammar mistakes rather than content. I ended up doing several examples as a class with the permission of the report author. □

This step was met with resistance by my class. They were pleased with their reports and proud of how much they had learned. The project was finished in their minds! Many made minimal changes to their reports. Next time, I would be sure students understood from the beginning that they would be revising their reports. □

student page

3 Providing Feedback on a Partner's Report

As partners give feedback on each other's reports, encourage them to write their comments in a positive way. You may also want students to limit their suggestions to the two or three they feel are most important.

This peer feedback helps students focus on quality in their own work as well as in their partner's work, and gives them ideas for revisions before turning in their final reports. You may want students to use the Assessment Rubric on pages A18–A19 as a checklist for looking over their partners' reports. An alternative to this step is to quickly check students' reports to make sure they are on the right track before beginning their revisions.

student page

4 Revising the Report

After students have revised their reports, you might want them to present their recommendations to the class. They could also create displays of their work to post around the classroom.

On page 48 in the Student Guide, there is a gallery of photographs picturing classroom scenes from the unit.

what to look for

DO STUDENTS' REPORTS INCLUDE:

- *clearly written recommendation(s)?*
- *the information that was used to make the recommendation(s)?*
- *an explanation of how the recommendation(s) will increase profits?*

See *Getting Down to Business* Assessment pages A18–A19 for assessment information.

Feedback

① spelled studying wrong

②. How will you increase attendance? You will either have to advertise more or do something else to get people to come. So your ____ ____ increase.

Report on Increasing Profit

...er carefully studying North Mall Cinema's income and expenses, I ...eve either of the following recommendations would increase profit to ...0,000 per day.

Increase attendance at the theaters. The theaters hold 300 people each. ...each of them have four showtimes, you could have 1200 people in each ...eater each day. Instead you have 575. Increasing adult attendance to ...00 and child attendance to 175 would give you a profit of $10,280 per day. To do this you might have to advertise in the beginning. This would increase your expenses but only temporarily. Once people got in the havit of coming to your theater you could stop your advertising again. This would mean that you would increase your income permanenetly while only tempoarily increasing your expenses, so your profit would go up.

2. You could also raiser profits to at least $10,000 a day by a combining raising prices and lowering movie rental expenses. Raise the price to $7.50 per adult and $4.50 for children. Find a company to rent movies more cheaply or show movies that are cheaper to rent. If you can pay $750 instead of $1,000 per movie your profit will be $10,130 per day. People don't mind paying $7.50 for a movie. This would increase your income by increasing the price. Renting cheaper movies would decrease your expenses. Increasing income and lowering expenses both increase profit.

3. Another way to increase your profit is to increase both attendance and the price while reducing expenses at the same time. Our spreadsheet shows that if you had 550 adults and 125 children at the show and raised the adult price to $6.25 you would increase income to $15,750. Then you could reduce your employee number to 16, eliminating one employee per ...ing. rent movies that cost only $800 and decrease maintenance costs ...result in a daily profit of $10,254. In this example, you ...g all expenses and therefore increase

---

Provide Feedback on a Partner's Report

Read your partner's report carefully and write some ways it could be improved. Here are suggestions to help you get started:

- I really like how you did . . .
- Some things you could improve are . . .
- I had trouble understanding what you meant by . . .
- The part that seemed unclear to me was when you said . . .

What suggestions do you have for helping your partner improve his or her work?

Revise the Report

Read your partner's feedback on your report. Think about your partner's suggestions and your own ideas for improving your report. Then revise your report. When you have finished revising your report, pull together these pieces of your final project:

- your revised report
- your original report
- your spreadsheet design on paper
- your spreadsheet printout
- your what-if questions

hot **words** | income
expense

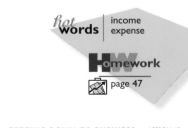

H•**W**omework

page 47

GETTING DOWN TO BUSINESS LESSON 12
© Creative Publications • MathScape **35**

A TEACHER REFLECTS

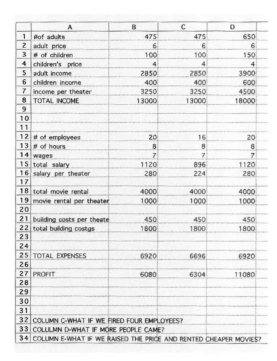

	A	B	C	D
1	#of adults	475	475	650
2	adult price	6	6	6
3	# of children	100	100	150
4	children's price	4	4	4
5	adult income	2850	2850	3900
6	children income	400	400	600
7	income per theater	3250	3250	4500
8	TOTAL INCOME	13000	13000	18000
9				
10				
11				
12	# of employees	20	16	20
13	# of hours	8	8	8
14	wages	7	7	7
15	total salary	1120	896	1120
16	salary per theater	280	224	280
17				
18	total movie rental	4000	4000	4000
19	movie rental per theater	1000	1000	1000
20				
21	building costs per theate	450	450	450
22	total building costgs	1800	1800	1800
23				
24				
25	TOTAL EXPENSES	6920	6696	6920
26				
27	PROFIT	6080	6304	11080
28				
29				
30				
31				
32	COLUMN C-WHAT IF WE FIRED FOUR EMPLOYEES?			
33	COLUMN D-WHAT IF MORE PEOPLE CAME?			
34	COLUMN E-WHAT IF WE RAISED THE PRICE AND RENTED CHEAPER MOVIES?			

Spreadsheets from Scratch?!

One of the reasons I really liked the final project was due to the mathematically significant what-if questions the students asked. They asked a wide range of questions that would result in changes on their spreadsheets, such as raising the price for adults to $10 and children to $8, paying the employees one-half of their salary, and decreasing the building costs by $300 per day. Because students had to use the work that they had already created for other parts of the project, I had students hold all of their work and turn it in at the completion of the phase. However, I did have a checklist so I could check for misconceptions and completion at various points as students were working on the final project.

My students had difficulty in the beginning of this phase. Because it was the first time they had to organize a spreadsheet from scratch, we had to come back together and talk about this. Students were simply going to put three columns on their spreadsheet and label them profit, income, and expenses. I started off the class discussion with, "Well, what do you need to figure out your profit?" Then I followed up by asking, "What do you need to figure out your income? expenses?" I asked students to tell me what all the elements were in this North Mall Cinema scenario that contributed to income and expenses. Students knew that profit, income, and expenses were crucial, but forgot to enter a formula for them.

In order to enter a formula, they needed other cells that gave them more information. I was fairly certain they were simply going to go through the Information About North Mall Cinema by hand or calculator. Why? Because of what they would formerly say to themselves: These are my expenses, so I'll add them up on paper and put them on the spreadsheet. Students were not allowing the spreadsheet to be a tool that was designed to do just that. After this class discussion, students put their heads together and came up with spreadsheets that had other columns.

Some of my students would try to use the "fill down" command and get the same answer. They knew it didn't make sense but didn't understand why this was happening. I would click on the cell, point to the formula bar, and show students that they didn't put a formula in. I would then point out that "fill down" only works if they put a formula in.

In this last phase particularly, I found that group cooperation was very important since students had to work together on computers. This was a positive experience for students and for me because the computer was of high interest to the students. Students were very proud of their projects and so were their parents, who shared their enthusiasm with me!

Assessment Overview

Many opportunities are offered in *Getting Down to Business* to assess students' conceptual understanding and skills related to representing functional relationships and organizing information. This unit contains embedded end-of-phase assessments in Lessons 3, 6, 9, and 12, the last serving as the unit assessment. To start the unit, have students complete the pre-assessment activity on Teacher's Guide page 6. Use this to assess readiness and growth throughout the unit when compared to students' work in Lesson 11. Also, you will find one skill quiz per phase on Reproducible pages R2–R5. Guidance for optional portfolios is found on pages A22–A23.

The *MathScape* assessment system has been designed to provide flexibility and support for educators in a variety of situations. The core system uses three assessment tools to help you gather information, allowing you to monitor students' individual growth throughout the unit and evaluate their knowledge and abilities at the unit end. Notes from the classroom share teachers' observations about student work, work evaluation, and ways to involve students in the assessment process. Teachers who have adapted this system have found it easy to meet their students' needs.

Assessment

C O N T E N T S

ASSESSMENT TOOLS

The three assessment tools—**What To Look For, Assessment Rubric, and Skill Check**—provide information for fully evaluating your students' learning. The information at the left shows where in the unit you can use each type of tool and on which assessment page it is described.

What To Look For

The What To Look For questions, which appear on the Teacher's Guide pages, are a short list of what students should be able to do at the end of an investigation. Use the questions as you lead a class discussion, monitor small group activities, or quickly check student work. The Assessment pages for these lessons provide an overview of student work along with teachers' observations.

Assessment Rubric

The Assessment Rubric describes what student work might look like at each of four different levels. An Assessment Rubric is provided for each phase assessment and the unit assessment, where it is accompanied by student work and teachers' notes from the classroom. A reproducible of the Assessment Criteria, corresponding to level 3 of the Assessment Rubric, is also available for student use. A general assessment rubric is provided for evaluating portfolios, which are an optional part of the assessment system.

Skill Check

The Skill Check helps you plan homework in the upcoming phase and review essential skills. It also provides the solutions for the Skill Quiz, a one-page reproducible quiz for each phase that focuses on the specific skills introduced or practiced in that phase. Teachers' notes contain suggestions on ways you can use the assessment information you gather to inform instruction.

Reporting to Parents

Although not in itself an assessment tool, the Reporting to Parents page brings together the rich information gathered by the What To Look For, Assessment Rubric, and Skill Check tools, and provides guidance in assigning letter grades. If you need to assign one grade for the unit, the information gathered from the different assessment tools can be recorded on the Assessment Checklist (page A3) to help you maintain a balance between concepts, skills, and processes.

ASSESSMENT CHECKLIST

The Assessment Checklist is on Reproducible page R1. You can use it to record the information gathered about each student with the different assessment tools and to note your observations. You can also give students their own copies of the checklist that they can use to organize and reflect on their work for their portfolios.

Because I only had eight computers in my classroom and limited use of the school computer lab, I found that I needed to monitor students who were not using the computer. I used the Assessment Checklist to help students keep track of the different types of assignments as they worked independently, and also to keep track of their computer time. Students signed off in the assessment column each time they used the computer. When a group was ready for the computer, I checked to see if their work was completed and signed each checklist. This way I could ensure equitable use of the computers, while monitoring students' classwork and homework. □

I use the Assessment Checklist to let parents know what their children have accomplished during the unit. For all students, I use a checklist to keep track of scores and notes related to their daily work. Then, at the end of the unit, I send a copy home to parents. It's a good way to communicate to parents what the students have learned. □

Getting Down to Business ASSESSMENT CHECKLIST

Period: Date:

Name:	Assignment Description	Assessment	Notes
Lesson		OK	more math tools
Pre-assessment	What math is used to increase profits?	—	homework late
Lesson 1	To Sell or Not to Sell Gourmet Hot Dogs	+	
Lesson 2	A Food Booth at a School Fair	3	
Lesson 3	What-If Questions for the Food Booth	75%	work on communication
Phase One Skill Check	Skill Quiz 1 & Homework 1–3	+	
Lesson 4	What-If Questions on Spreadsheets	—	
Lesson 5	"What's My Formula?" Game	4	conceptual sophistication
Lesson 6	Double Your Profits?	80%	
Phase Two Skill Check	Skill Quiz 2 & Homework 4–6	+	
Lesson 7	How Many Sales at Tee-Time?	—	homework missing
Lesson 8	How Much Profit at Tee-Time?	3	
Lesson 9	Monthes Later at Tee-Time	90%	
Phase Three Skill Check	Skill Quiz 3 & Homework 7–9		
Lesson 10	North Mall Cinema's Project		
Lesson 11	North Mall Cinema's Spreadsheet	3+	creative spreadsheet but missing a formula
Lesson 12	North Mall Cinema's Report	90%	
Phase Four Skill Check	Skill Quiz 4 & Homework 10–12	OK	growth in tools
Post-assessment	What math is used to increase profits?		
Comments:	Showed good skill growth in using PIE formula and technology tools. He is inconsistent in checking over his work—sometimes showing good attention to detail (Lesson 7) and other times making careless computational mistakes (Lesson 2). Focus on taking time necessary to complete all assignments.		

I was surprised at the narrow range of tools students used to make calculations. Most students chose paper and pencil with only a few trying the calculator. Some students did not have any ideas about what elements go into a business and how those elements interact to make a profit. □

WHAT TO LOOK FOR

Pre-assessment

You can use the Pre-assessment on page 6 of the Teacher's Guide to assess the prerequisites for the unit. At the end of the unit, you can compare this task to the work from Lesson 11 to note growth that has occurred in the course of the unit. (See Post-assessment, page A21.)

DO STUDENTS' PRE-ASSESSMENTS DEMONSTRATE THE PREREQUISITES OF:

- ability to organize data into tables?

- knowledge of basic skills necessary to use a calculator?

- understanding of what formulas are and how to write equations?

- familiarity with creating and reading line graphs?

Bake Sale

Baked Goods
Signs
Booth
Napkins / Plates

25¢ per item
10¢ per sign (5 signs)
free
$10 (total)

I would figure out the price I wanted to charge for each cupcake (75¢). Then I would subtract the price I'm charging from the price I bought it for. (50¢). I would subtract the cost of the signs and plates + napkins. from the total amount made from the sales. Then I would use a calculator to figure out the profit of everything. I would have to make about $110.50 or sell about 221 cupcakes at $.75. That would be a total of $165.75 minus $25 per cupcake (the cost I paid for it). ($41.44) That would be $124.31 minus $10.50 for the signs, plates, + napkins. The profit then would be $113.81. A little more than the targeted $100.

Phase One: Lessons 1 & 2

The student work from Lessons 1 and 2 of this phase should show an increased understanding of the Profit = Income − Expenses relationship. One common problem to look for in students' work is a poor understanding of expenses—what they are and where they fit into this relationship.

Most students were still unsure about the relation-ship between income, profit, and expenses. Many of them would forget to deduct the cost of items when they were calculating the profit. To help students understand how different tools could be used to make calcu-lations, I had them complete the simulation in Lesson 2 with paper and pencil the first time through, and with a calculator the second time through. □

Thank you for taking your time to read this letter, and I hope you take my advice.

Dear Students,

Your hot-dog stand is a wonderful idea, but there are a few drawbacks in your decisions. You said that each hot-dog would cost $2.00, & I totally disagree with that decision because no one will pay that much, even for a gourmet hot-dog. Also, why did you make advertising flyers? I personally see no point to that, all it is, is one more expense, & one more debt. The sign for your booth was an obvious choice, but that would mean you don't need the flyers.

Compare the Results of the Two Simulations

1. We made many decisions while running this business. The price we chose for booth games was $ .40 each for one chocolate chip cookie. In the first game we bought 325 cookies for our inventory. The second game we bought 25 cookies less than the first game. We purchased 300. We made decisions about hiring and buying more cookies. We did hire another person but did not purchase more cookies.

2. The choices we did different in the first game was that in the first game we bought more inventory than in the second game. The next different decision was to buy more cookies. In the first game we did not buy more inventory but in the second game we did. Everything else we did the same.

3. The final profit from both games are different. In the first game we made around $36. In the second game, however, we made about $44. We made almost $10 more than in the first game.

4. The decisions I think made the difference in determining the profit was the decision to cut the amount of inventory. Since we cut the amount of inventory we did not have as much cookies to sell. The reason I think this is because we had more money left over to help raise the amount earned, also known as profit.

One student pre-sented the report in a business letter form and included a chart showing the profit, income, and expenses. The student clearly explained the steps involved in calculating profit, and showed all of the calculations correctly. I gave this student a 4. □

I gave the student a 3 if the report was complete, but there were a few minor errors in the calculations or the student's explanation of the profit, income, and expenses was very brief and did not show a sophisticated understanding of the relationship. □

In one case, the student had good suggestions for income and expenses, but there were some errors in the calculations shown. I also noticed that this student was having some difficulty generating appropriate what-if questions and making a connection between profit, income, and expenses. I gave the work a 2. □

For the embedded assessment in Lesson 3, What-If Questions for the Food Booth, students applied what they had learned in Phase One to identify income and expenses, and calculate income and profit. The Assessment Rubric on the opposite page is designed to help you evaluate student work. See Reproducible page R6 for a version of the level 3 assessment criteria worded for student use.

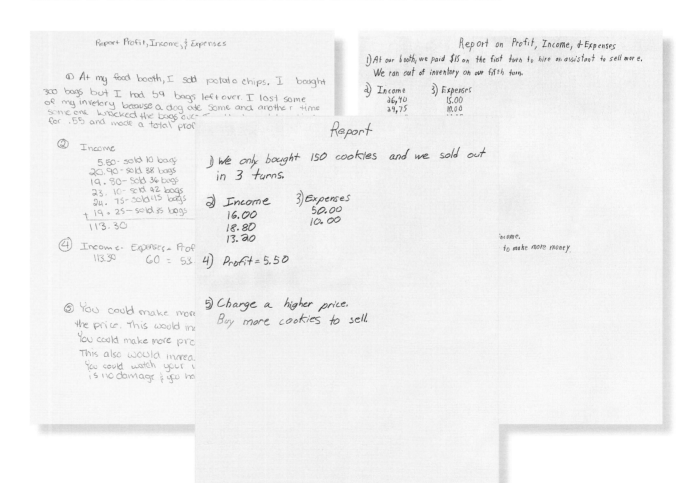

Does student work...

- include examples of income and expenses for their food booth beyond the requirements of the assignment?

- show calculations of profit and income with no mathematical errors?

- include detailed description of the steps to calculate income and profit?

- include diagrams or charts to show the relationship between profit and income?

- display a sophisticated understanding of how changing income and/or expenses will increase profit?

Goes beyond expectations

- include examples of income and expenses for their food booth required for assignment?

- show calculations of profit with no significant mathematical errors?

- show calculations of income with no significant mathematical errors?

- include a clear description in their own words of the steps involved in calculating income and profit?

- display a basic understanding of how changing income and/or expenses will increase profit?

Meets all expectations

- contain at least two examples of income and expenses for their food booth?

- show calculations of profit with some mathematical errors?

- show calculations of income with some mathematical errors?

- include calculations only for income and profit with no written description?

- reveal misunderstandings about how changing income and/or expenses will increase profit?

Meets some expectations

- contain only one example of income and one example of expenses for their food booth?

- include few calculations of profit or calculations with major mathematical errors?

- include few calculations of income or calculations with major mathematical errors?

- display a lack of understanding about how changing income and/or expenses will increase profit?

Falls below expectations

SKILL CHECK

Phase One: Homework & Quiz

Students' conceptual understanding in Phase One is monitored daily using the **What To Look For** and evaluated using the **Assessment Rubric.** The lesson homework and the **Phase One Skill Quiz** are tools to check skill proficiency.

Homework

Homework for Lessons 1–3 appears in the Student Guide on pages 36–38. Answers for this homework are on Assessment pages A29–A31. Depending on the needs of your students, you may assign all or part of the homework for each lesson. You may want to take students' homework performance into consideration as part of the overall phase evaluation.

Skill Quiz

The Phase One Skill Quiz is provided on Reproducible page R2. Answers are given here. Hot Topics for Phase One are:

- Using and Finding Percents
- Analyzing Data
- Integer Operations
- Collecting Data
- If/Then Statements
- Evaluating Expressions and Formulas

SKILL QUIZ ANSWERS

1. Income is a, f; Expenses are b, c, d, e, g, h.

2. a. $795.00

   b. $1,299.00

   c. $504.00

3. $P = I - E$

4. some amount less than $1.25 so the owner can make a profit

5. $65.00

6. $10.00 profit from one book, $200.00 profit from 20 books

7. Yes, profit can be a negative number. Answers will vary. Expenses must be greater than income for profit to be negative.

Phase Two: Lessons 4 & 5

The student work from Lessons 4 and 5 of this phase should show an increased understanding of, and expertise with, using spreadsheets on the computer. One error to look for in students' work is a lack of understanding of a spreadsheet as a tool in itself. Students may be trying to use a spreadsheet as a table where they calculate data and enter it into the spreadsheet rather than allow the spreadsheet to do the calculations.

Because some students were used to formulas looking a particular way, they had trouble remembering to enter an equal sign (=) before the formula on the spreadsheet. Other students had no experience with formulas and needed extra practice. I used the hot words/hot topics handbook *to give these students this needed practice.* ☐

Price	Profit	Total Profit
0.4	70	272.5
0.5	122.5	If you raise your price 10 cents the price profit, and total profit increases by 10 cents
0.4	100	

Price	Expenses	Profit
.4E		
.55		
.45		

Total
2

Exploring what-if Questions

No. Sold	Profit	Total Profit
1200	180	795
1500	37.5	If we sell double the amount the no. sold the profit and the total profit increases
1600	240	

No. Sold	Profit	Total Profit
300	45	198.75
375	93.75	If half as many people come, the no. sold, the profit, and the total profit decreases by half.
400	60	

Expenses	Profit	Total Profit
180	120	575
225	275	If the expenses double, the expenses, profit, and total profit double, increase
240	0	

	No. Sold	Profit	Total Profit
PC	0	-90	217.50
CCC	750	187.50	If nobody buys potatoe chips the total profit will decrease
P	800	120	and there will be one less thing on no. Sold and profit.

• The new things I learned about a spreadsheet are the only way a formula works is when you have a (=) sign in front of it.
    you can only get income, expences & profit is by typing in a formula.

• There was nothing real confusing about this assignment to me.

• One helpful tip is to get a cell to show up click on it really quick instead of typing it in. And also it would go faster if you have one person type the letters & some one type the #'s.

*Work was a 4
when it was evident
that the student
had spent time
looking for places where formulas
could be used more efficiently,
especially when the formulas were
all correct and the student's explanations showed that the concept of
formulas was understood.* ☐

*Sita showed an understanding of
when to use formulas and when to
just type in numbers in the spreadsheet. She came close to doubling
her profits so I gave her a 3.* ☐

*I gave the work a 2 if the student
still needed to work on entering
formulas in the spreadsheet or
knew to sometimes use formulas
and sometimes use numbers, but
was confused when to use which.
For example, a formula should not
appear in the Number Sold
column.* ☐

4 3 2 1 ASSESSMENT RUBRIC
Phase Two: Lesson 6

In Lesson 6, Double Your Profits, students created a spreadsheet on the computer and analyzed it to show their understanding of spreadsheets and formulas. The Assessment Rubric on the opposite page is designed to help you evaluate student work. See Reproducible page R6 for a version of the level 3 assessment criteria worded for student use.

	A	B	C	D	E	F	G	H
1	BOOTH	NUMBER SOLD	PRICE	INCOME	EXPENSES	PROFIT		
2								
3	potato chips	67	$0.40	$26.80	$5.00	$21.80		
4	potato chips	134	$0.40	$53.60	$5.00	$48.60		
5	potato chips	67	$0.85	$56.95	$5.00	$51.95		
6	potato chips	67	$0.60	$40.20	$0.00	$40.20		

1. What if we doubled the number sold and our expenses stayed the same? Our profit more than doubled.

2. What if we raised the price to $.85 and our expenses stayed the same? Our profit in

3. What if we got all the items donated and raised the prices by $.20? Our profit almost but not quite.

ANALYZE YOUR SPREADSHEET

1. For columns, we put booth, number sold, price, income, expenses, and profit. For rows, we put potato chips. For income, we used number sold times price. For example, =B5*C5. Then we used fill down for the rest of this column. For profit we used income minus expenses. For example, =D5–E5. We also used fill down so the spreadsheet would put the formulas for the rest of the profit.

We decided when to use formulas by knowing which columns changed based on numbers in other columns.

A formula tells the computer how to find the answer for the cell. You tell the computer which cells to use and whether to add, subtract, multiply, or divide. The formula makes it easy to see what would happen if something changes in your business because you don't have to type in the numbers again. For example, if you want to change the price, you can see right away how that changes the income.

2. What if we doubled the number sold and our expenses stayed the same? What if we raised the price to $.85 and our expenses stayed the same? What if we got all the items donated and raised the prices by $.20?

3. Someone else would test one of the what-if questions by starting with our original numbers and doing what the question says. For the first question, multiply each number in the number sold column by 2 to get the new number sold and see what happened to profit.

Does student work...

- include an original spreadsheet that goes beyond the requirements of the assignment?

- show formulas written correctly in spreadsheet notation that reveal a sophisticated understanding of profit, income, and expenses relationship?

- include a sophisticated explanation of what a formula is, and when and where to use one?

- contain more than three what-if questions with a clear explanation of the meaning of the questions?

- include an original spreadsheet that meets the requirements of the assignment?

- show formulas written correctly in spreadsheet notation?

- include an explanation in the student's own words of what a formula is, and when and where to use one?

- contain three what-if questions with a clear explanation of the meaning of the questions?

- include an original spreadsheet that does not meet all of the requirements of the assignment?

- have formulas written in spreadsheet notation with some errors?

- include an explanation in the student's own words of what a formula is?

- contain three what-if questions with no explanation of the meaning of the questions?

- include an original spreadsheet that is incomplete and disorganized?

- have formulas written in spreadsheet notation with major errors?

- include fewer than three what-if questions with no explanation of the meaning of the questions?

 Goes beyond expectations

 Meets all expectations

 **Meets some expectations**

 **Falls below expectations**

Assessment

*Many of my stu-
dents did not have
strong computer
skills. I carefully
chose the groups so that there was
a balance of strong skills and weak
skills. I then encouraged students
to help one another on the computer. I also held two after-school
sessions for students who wanted
extra practice.* □

SKILL CHECK

Phase Two: Homework & Quiz

Students' conceptual understanding in Phase Two is monitored daily using the **What To Look For** and evaluated using the **Assessment Rubric**. The lesson homework and the **Phase Two Skill Quiz** are ways to check skill proficiency.

Homework

Homework for Lessons 4–6 appears in the Student Guide on pages 39–41. Answers for this homework are on Assessment pages A32–A34. Depending on the needs of your students, you may assign all or part of the homework for each lesson. You may want to take students' homework performance into consideration as part of the overall phase evaluation.

Skill Quiz

The Phase Two Skill Quiz is provided on Reproducible page R3. Answers are given here. Hot Topics for Phase Two are:

- Spreadsheets
- Four-Function Calculator
- Order of Operations
- If/Then Statements

SKILL QUIZ ANSWERS

1. C
2. F3
3. B5*C5
4. $994.25
5. G3, G4, and G5
6. by multiplying numbers in column B by numbers in column E; =B4*E4
7. Answers will vary. One possibility is to increase the price of white paper. Increase the price of white paper as much as you can without causing the number of sheets sold to go down.
8. Answers will vary. Note: The cost-to-price ratio for white paper is about the same as for colored paper and greater than for card stock. Students may cite these ratios to support their choices.

Phase Three: Lessons 7 & 8

The student work from Lessons 7 and 8 of this phase should show an increased understanding of the effect of price and number of sales on expenses and income, and therefore, on profit. One common problem to look for in students' work is that students may have difficulty understanding how data on the graphs and spreadsheets are related.

Some students wanted to connect the dots on their graphs in Lesson 7. I pointed out that although their calculations might show that there were 2.5 T-shirts, you could not have .5 of a T-shirt. I drew a graph on the board and connected the dots to make it a line graph. Then I showed the class how this implied that you could have fractional parts of a T-shirt, which in reality you could not. This seemed to help students better understand why the dots should not be connected. ☐

Analyze the Graphs

1. Price vs. Income: It forms a upside down "V". The graph changes direction at $19 when people won't buy the T-shirts anymore because of the high prices. Therefore the income goes down.

Price vs. Expenses: It is a straight line because the expenses stay the same.

Price vs. Profit: It forms a upside down "V" too. Profit starts going down when people won't buy the shirts.

2. When the price goes up the income goes up until we reach the price of $19 dallors after which the income goes down. The same thing happens for profit. For profit and income when price changes they change too. When price goes up too much, they start going down. Expenses don't change no matter what price you charge.

3. Income and profit go up when the number you sell goes up. They go up when the price goes up till you raise the price too high and people won't buy. Expenses don't change that much.

4. The profit did not fall below zero. There were always enough people to buy the shirt to keep profit above zero.

5. I think Tee Time should charge $19 because that is when they made the most profit.

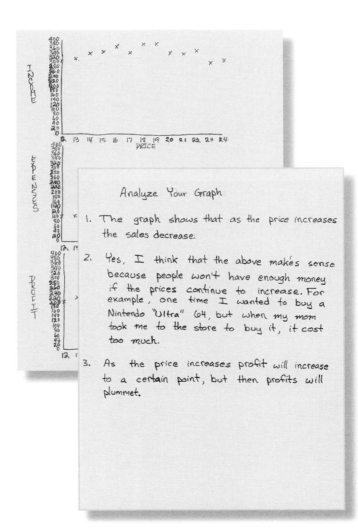

Analyze Your Graph

1. The graph shows that as the price increases the sales decrease.

2. Yes, I think that the above makes sense because people won't have enough money if the prices continue to increase. For example, one time I wanted to buy a Nintendo "Ultra" 64, but when my mom took me to the store to buy it, it cost too much.

3. As the price increases profit will increase to a certain point, but then profits will plummet.

Assessment

Phase Three: Lesson 9

If the student was able to complete all of the graphs, explain clearly the relationship between profit, income, and expenses, and show a great deal of sophisticated mathematical understanding, I gave the student a 4. □

If all of the requirements were met, but the mathematical understandings were very basic and the student completed the graphs and explained how profit, income, and expenses were connected on each graph, I gave the student a 3. □

One of my students had completed the graphs and explanations, but still was not clear about the relationship between profit, income, and expenses. Because of this, I gave this student a 2. □

In Lesson 9, Months Later at Tee-Time, students applied what they had learned in Phase Three about graphs and the profit, income, and expenses relationship to explain how the income and expenses graphs result in the profit graph. The Assessment Rubric on the opposite page is designed to help you evaluate student work. See Reproducible page **R6** for a version of the level 3 assessment criteria worded for student use.

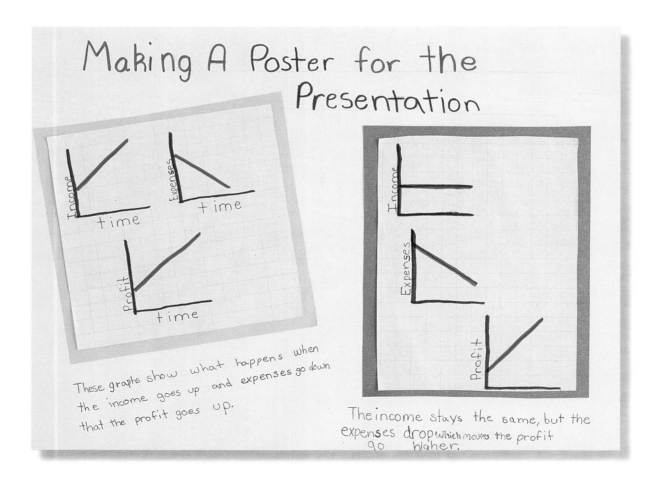

Does student work...

- include two or three sets of mathematically sophisticated profit, income, and expenses graphs on a poster?

- contain clear and concise explanations of each individual graph using charts or diagrams as necessary?

- show a detailed explanation of the relationships between the three graphs that shows an understanding beyond expectations of the relationship among profit, income, and expenses?

- include two or three sets of profit, income, and expense graphs?

- contain written explanations for each individual graph?

- show an explanation of the relationships between the three graphs that shows a basic understanding of the relationship among profit, income, and expenses?

- include two or three sets of profit, income, and expense graphs?

- contain a brief explanation of each individual graph?

- show a brief explanation of the relationships between the three graphs that describes the relationship among profit, income, and expenses with some misconceptions?

- contain an incomplete or disorganized set of profit, income, and expense graphs?

- include an incomplete explanation of each individual graph?

- show inaccurate or incomplete explanations of the relationships between the three graphs?

 Goes beyond expectations

 Meets all expectations

 Meets some expectations

 Falls below expectations

SKILL CHECK

Phase Three: Homework & Quiz

Your students' conceptual understanding in Phase Three was monitored daily using the **What To Look For** and evaluated using the Assessment Rubric. The lesson homework and the Phase Three Skill Quiz are tools to check skill proficiency.

Homework

Homework for Lessons 7–9 appears in the Student Guide on pages 42–44. Answers for this homework are on Assessment pages A35–A37. Depending on the needs of your students, you may assign all or part of the homework for each lesson. You may want to take students' homework performance into consideration as part of the overall phase evaluation.

Skill Quiz

The Phase Three Skill Quiz is available on Reproducible page R4. Answers are given here. Hot Topics for Phase Three are:

- Collecting Data
- Graphing on the Coordinate Plane
- Integer Operations
- Displaying Data
- Analyzing Data

SKILL QUIZ ANSWERS

1. $8.95

2. The largest income is earned at $14.95.

	A	B	C
1	Price of Toy Boat	Number of People Who Want to Buy Toy Boat at This Price	Income from the Sale of Toy Boat
2	$ 8.95	1,000	$ 8,950.00
3	$14.95	680	$10,166.00
4	$32.95	250	$ 8,237.50

3. As price increases, income decreases.

4. **a.** Price vs. Income. Explanations will vary.

5. **c.** Price vs. Profit. Explanations will vary.

6. **a.** and **b.** Price vs. Income and Cost vs. Price. Explanations will vary.

7. **b.** and **c.** Price vs. Cost and Profit vs. Price. Explanations will vary.

8.

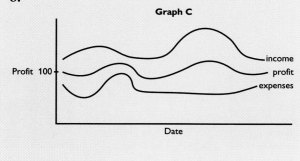

Graph C

Profit 100

income
profit
expenses

Date

Phase Four: Lessons 10 & 11

The student work from Lessons 10 and 11 of this phase should show an increased understanding of the relationship between profit, income, and expenses as they analyze the case study of the **North Mall Cinema** and build a spreadsheet from scratch to make recommendations. **One common problem to look for in students' work is that students may have difficulty identifying and organizing all of the pieces of information necessary for the spreadsheet.**

Since this was the first time that students had built a spreadsheet from scratch, they had trouble figuring out what columns they needed to calculate profit, income, and expenses. Some of the students wanted their spreadsheets to have only those three columns: profit, income, and expenses. We brainstormed as a class the elements needed to determine income (number sold, price) and expenses (number sold, cost). This helped those students who needed to set up the necessary columns on their spreadsheet. □

What If Questions to Explore

1. What if more people came to the show?
2. What if they fired some of their employees?
3. What if they raised the prices?
4. What if they found a cheaper company to rent movies from?
5. What if they added a show in the morning?
6. What if they paid their employees less money?
7. What if they showed more new movies?

QUESTIONS WE THINK WOULD HAVE THE GREATEST IMPACT
1. What if more people came to the show?
2. What if they found a cheaper company to rent movies from?
3. What if they raised the prices?

NORTH MALL CINEMA'S PROJECT

INCOME

4 SHOWS WITH 475 ADULTS AND 100 CHILDREN PER DAY

475 X $6.00 = $2850
100 X $4.00 = $400

2850 + 400= 3250

$3250 X 4 shows = $13,000 = TOTAL INCOME PER DAY

EXPENSES

20 EMPLOYEES FOR 8 HOURS A DAY AT $7.00 AN HOUR

8 X 7 = 56

56 X 20 = $1120

$1,000 PER MOVIE RENTAL

1000 X 4 = $4,000

$1800 PER DAY BUILDING COSTS AND UTILITIES

$1120 (EMPLOYEES) + $4000 (MOVIE RENTAL) + $1800 (BUILDING COSTS AND UTILITIES = $6920 = TOTAL EXPENSES PER DAY

	A	B	C	D	E
1	#of adults	475	475	650	475
2	adult price	6	6	6	7.5
3	# of children	100	100	150	100
4	children's price	4	4	4	4.5
5	adult income	2850	2850	3900	3562.5
6	children income	400	400	600	450
7	income per theater	3250	3250	4500	4012.5
8	TOTAL INCOME	13000	13000	18000	16050
9					
10					
11					
12	# of employees	20	16	20	20
13	# of hours	8	8	8	8
14	wages	7	7	7	7
15	total salary	1120	896	1120	1120
16	salary per theater	280	224	280	280
17					
18	total movie rental	4000	4000	4000	3000
19	movie rental per theater	1000	1000	1000	750
20					
21	building costs per theate	450	450	450	450
22	total building costs	1800	1800	1800	1800
23					
24					
25	TOTAL EXPENSES	6920	6696	6920	5920
26					
27	PROFIT	6080	6304	11080	10130
28					
29					
30					
31					
32	COLUMN C-WHAT IF WE FIRED FOUR EMPLOYEES?				
33	COLULMN D-WHAT IF MORE PEOPLE CAME?				
34	COLUMN E-WHAT IF WE RAISED THE PRICE AND RENTED CHEAPER MOVIES?				

I gave one of my students a 4 because the report showed how the student had made quite sophisticated mathematical connections. The what-if questions revealed many diverse and complex ways to increase profit. This student plugged the computer into a large monitor and demonstrated "fill down" for the whole class. ☐

One of the reports was complete and accurate with only a few minor errors, but did not show the depth of mathematical understanding necessary to make it a 4. Some of the what-if questions were not targeted to affect the profit, income, and expenses relationship. I gave this student a 3. ☐

If the report was complete, but the formulas were sometimes incorrect or some columns that should have had formulas had numbers instead, I gave the student a 2. ☐

4 3 2 1

ASSESSMENT RUBRIC

Phase Four: Lessons 12

In Lesson 12, North Mall Cinema's Report, students applied what they had learned in the unit to create a report that contained recommendations for improving profits, exchange it with their partners, and make revisions. The Assessment Rubric on the opposite page is designed to help you evaluate student work. See Reproducible page R6 for a version of the level 3 assessment criteria worded for student use.

NORTH MALL CINEMA PROJECT

After studying the numbers from North Mall Cinma, I would like to make two recommendations. Either of my recommendations would increase your profit to $10,000 a day, which is your goal.

1. You should increase your attendance to 550 adults and 125 children per day. At the same time, raise the price to $7.00 for adults and $4.50 for children. Since you already have 475 adults and 100 children I don't think that would be too hard. To get more people to come, give better service. You could have the employees bring the popcorn and other snacks to the customers instead of making
have enough employees so this woul
Raising the price can be tricky beca
raise the price so high that people g
$7.00 is about average and people
this, you will increase your income a
increase since your expenses stay th

2. Another suggestion I have is to
with raising the price. This way yo
increase the number of poeple who c
movie for $750 instead of $1000. J
and reduce building maintenance to
suggested in #1. Your profit will be
suggestion means increasing income
the same time so your profit will go

NORTH MALL CINEMA PROJECT

These are my ideas for increasing profit to $10,000.

1. Increase the prices to $8.50 for adults and $5.50 for kids. This would increase your income.

2. Increase the number of poeple to 650 adults and 150 kids. This would increase the income.

3. Reduce the number of employees to 4 and only pay them $6 per hour. Rent movies for $500 and only pay $800 for building maintenance. This would reduce all your expenses so you would increase your profit.

NORTH MALL CINEMA

Here are some ways to have $10,000 in profit each day.

You need more people to come to your theaters. If you had 650 adults and 150 children come each day, you would make $11,080 every day. That is because you would increase your income. Your expenses wouldn't change unless you had to advertise. But you have $180 ti spend on advertising and still have $10,000 profit.

You need to raise your prices. You should do a survey to find out how much money people would pay to go to a show. If you charged $8.00 for adults and $4.50 for children you would make $10,080 a day. Your theaters are comfortable and you have good popcorn so we think people would pay $8.00. We don't think you should charge more than $4.50 for kids.

Does student work...

- include an accurate and sophisticated spreadsheet that went beyond the requirements of the assignment?

- show formulas in spreadsheet notation in appropriate columns with no errors?

- contain innovative what-if questions that relate to the spreadsheet or real world data?

- include clearly written recommendations that make mathematical connections?

- contain an explanation using diagrams of how each recommendation will make profits increase?

 Goes beyond expectations

- include an accurate and well-organized spreadsheet that shows income, expenses, and profits?

- show formulas in spreadsheet notation in appropriate columns with no significant errors?

- contain what-if questions that relate to the spreadsheet?

- include clearly written recommendations based on data from the spreadsheet?

- contain an explanation of how each recommendation will make profits increase?

 Meets all expectations

- include a spreadsheet showing income, expenses, and profits with some errors?

- show written formulas in spreadsheet notation in appropriate columns with some errors?

- contain what-if questions that do not clearly relate to the spreadsheet?

- include written recommendations that are not based on the spreadsheet?

- contain a brief explanation of how at least one recommendation will make profits increase?

 Meets some expectations

- contain an incomplete spreadsheet, or a spreadsheet with major mathematical errors?

- include written formulas with many mistakes in either spreadsheet notation or placement?

- contain incomplete what-if questions that have no connection to the spreadsheet?

- include an explanation of a recommendation that shows a major misconception or is incomplete?

 Falls below expectations

The questions I
gave students to
reflect on their
projects in Phase
Four were the following:

- *How accurate do you think your formulas in your spreadsheets were?*
- *How complete were your descriptions of the profit, income, and expenses relationship?*
- *On a scale of 1–4 (4 being best), how would you rate your work on this project?*
- *If you were asked to design another spreadsheet from scratch, what would you do differently?* □

Phase Four: Homework & Quiz

Your students' conceptual understanding in Phase Four was monitored daily using the **What To Look For** and evaluated using the **Assessment Rubric**. The lesson homework and the **Phase Four Skill Quiz** are tools to check skill proficiency.

Homework

Homework for Lessons 10–12 appears in the Student Guide on pages 45–47. Answers for this homework are on Assessment pages A38–A40. Depending on the needs of your students, you may assign all or part of the homework for each lesson. You may want to take students' homework performance into consideration as part of the overall phase evaluation.

Skill Quiz

The Phase Four Skill Quiz is provided on Reproducible page R5. Answers are given here. Hot Topics for Phase Four are:

- Displaying Data
- If/Then Statements
- Size and Scale
- Spreadsheets
- Analyzing Data
- Square and Cube Roots

SKILL QUIZ ANSWERS

1. a. increase income by $28 by raising prices or selling more items

   b. decrease expenses by $28 by cutting costs

2. Answers will vary, but possibilities are:

   a. sell 200 cookies

   b. increase price to $1.75 each

   c. use a combination of ways, such as cutting expenses while increasing price of cookies

   d. use a combination of ways, such as increasing price and increasing number of cookies sold

3. Income must double as well. Example: If $I = 20$ and $E = 10$, then profit is 10. If $I = 40$ and $E = 20$, then profit is 20. (40 is 2×20)

4. Income must increase by 50%. Example: If $I = 20$ and $E = 10$, then profit is 10. If $I = 30$ and $E = 20$, then profit is 10. (30 is 20 plus 50% of 20.)

5. Expenses must double as well. Example: If $I = 30$ and $E = 10$, then profit is 20. If $I = 60$ and $E = 20$, then profit is 40. (20 is 2×10)

6. Profit will increase. Example: If $I = 30$ and $E = 10$, then profit is 20. If $I = 60$ and $E = 10$, then profit is 50.

7. Profit will decrease. Example: If $I = 30$ and $E = 10$, then profit is 20. If $I = 30$ and $E = 20$, then profit is 10.

8. Yes. Explanations will vary. Possible answer: Expenses = Income − Profit

9. =F2−D2   10. =B2*G2

11. Possibilities: =H2*.72; or =H2−H2*.28

Post-assessment

To get a sense of your students' growth over the course of the unit, you can compare students' pre-assessment work (see page A4) with Lesson 11 work. Ask students to write a second response to the question: What math is used to increase profit? Compare this to their pre-assessment writing.

DID STUDENTS DEMONSTRATE GROWTH IN:

- posing what-if questions based on spreadsheets?

- making recommendations based on spreadsheets?

- calculating income and profit?

- describing the relationship between income, expenses, and profit?

- reading and writing formulas in spreadsheet notation?

- organizing and relating data on tables, graphs, and spreadsheets?

The most obvious growth I observed was in the students' choice of tools. In Phase Four, students leaned more toward technology than they did in the pre-assessment activity, choosing a calculator and spreadsheet. Also, students better understood the business terms and used them in their explanations of the profit, income, and expenses relationship. □

	A	B	C	D	E	F	G	H
1	#of adults	adult price	# of children	chilren price				
2	475	$6.00	100	$4.00				
3	600	$6.00	175	$4.00	1. What if more people came to the show?			
4	475	$6.00	100	$4.00	2. What if they found a cheaper company to rent movies from?			
5	475	$8.00	100	$5.00	3. what if they raised the prices?			
6								
7	adult income	chilren income	income per theater	total income				
8	$2850.00	$400.00	$3250.00	$13000.00				
9	$3600.00	$700.00	$4300.00	$17200.00	1. What if more people came to the show?			
10	$2850.00	$400.00	$3250.00	$13000.00	2. What if they found a cheaper company to rent movies from?			
11	$3800.00	$500.00	$4300.00	$17200.00	3. what if they raised the prices?			
12								
13								
14								
15								
16								
17								
18								
19	#of employees	# of hours	wage		total salary	salary per theater		
20	20	8	$7.00	$1120.00	$280.00			
21	20	8	$7.00	$1120.00	$280.00	1. What if more people came to the show?		
22	20	8	$7.00	$1120.00	$280.00	2. What if they found a cheaper company to rent m		
23	20	8	$7.00	$1120.00	$280.00	3. what if they raised the prices?		
24								
25	movie rental per theater	total rental	build. cost per thea	total building costs				
26	$1000.00	$4000.00	$450.00	$1800.00				
27	$1000.00	$4000.00	$450.00	$1800.00	1. What if more people came to the show?			
28	$500.00	$2000.00	$450.00	$1800.00	2. What if they found a cheaper company to rent movies from?			
29	$1000.00	$4000.00	$450.00	$1800.00	3. what if they raised the prices?			
30								
31	total expenses	profit						
32	$6920.00	$6080.00						
33	$6920.00	$10280.00	1. What if more people came to the show?					
34	$4920.00	$8080.00	2. What if they found a cheaper company to rent movies from?					
35	$6920.00	$10280.00	3. what if they raised the prices?					

As I planned the lessons, I decided which activities would make a good portfolio activity. This ensured that all the strands and unifying ideas, as well as any other concepts I considered important, would be represented in the students' portfolios. The lessons in Getting Down to Business that had spreadsheets and graphs revealing something about the profit, income, and expenses relationship were the ones I designated to be included as portfolio work. Even though I had made the prior selection of work, students still needed to include a sentence or two regarding the assignment. I asked them to write what the assignment was about, what they learned, and why they thought I had them include this particular item in the portfolio. These statements told quite a bit about what the students had learned, and whether they understood the math in the lesson. □

Portfolio Review

The focus of the porfolio evaluation is to gain insight into students' growth over time and to see how they view themselves as mathematicians. The porfolio should show students' increasing ability to communicate mathematically, solve problems, and make mathematical connections. The Assessment Rubric on the opposite page is designed to help you evaluate student work.

FOR THIS UNIT THE FOLLOWING ITEMS WORK ESPECIALLY WELL TO SUPPLEMENT A STUDENT'S BASIC PORTFOLIO:

- Assessment Checklist

- teacher-completed checklists showing quality and quantity of daily work

- final project

- a photo or a printout, produced by the student or teacher, of a student's work.

Does the portfolio show...

- significant mathematical growth in understanding and application of unit goals?

- significant mathematical growth in skill development?

- creativity and quality of work that go beyond assignment requirements?

- timely completion of assignments?

- no significant mathematical errors in assigned work?

- clear, coherent, and thoughtful explanations of the mathematical process?

Goes beyond expectations

- some mathematical growth in understanding and application of unit goals?

- some mathematical growth in skill development?

- acceptable quality of work?

- timely completion of assignments?

- no significant mathematical errors in assigned work?

- clear explanations of mathematical process?

Meets all expectations

- an understanding and application of unit goals?

- skill development documented with little growth?

- inconsistent quality of work ?

- assignments complete but not always on time?

- minor mathematical errors in assigned work?

- unclear explanations of mathematical process?

Meets some expectations

- that key points in the understanding and application of unit goals were missed?

- that skill development is not documented?

- that the quality of work is consistently poor?

- that assignments are consistently late?

- significant mathematical errors in assigned work?

- no explanations of the mathematical process?

Falls below expectations

Assessment

I used the final project rubric to come up with a unit rubric. I added things like homework being on time, phase assessment scores, skill growth, and class participation. I then used this rubric to generate one score for the entire unit. I found that this way I could look at the final project and take into account the quality and quantity of the work that got the student to this point. I was also able to factor in student growth □

The amount of weight I give to the portfolio grade varies, depending on the type of portfolio used. The grade can be quite significant if the portfolio is a showcase portfolio presented to parents, teachers, or other adults. It can be worth as much as another test, because its purpose is to show growth over time, which some tests may measure also. Because the portfolio contains many items, it would seem appropriate to at least make the grade worth more than a homework or class assignment. □

Reporting to Parents

If you need to assign a single letter grade to reflect all the rich information students have gathered over the course of the unit, remember to maintain a balance between concepts, skills, and processes when doing so. In this particular unit, the final project is cumulative, and the rubric score from the project should be a large part of any grade given.

Skill Proficiency

By combining the Skill Checks, Homework, and any Handbook assignments, you should be able to demonstrate to parents their child's ability to practice the skills of solving equations, organizing data in graphs and tables, and posing what-if questions. Although these skills are an integral part of the daily lessons in this unit, Lesson 8, How Much Profit at Tee-Time?, in which students make graphs from spreadsheets, is an obvious example to show parents how skills are incorporated into an investigation.

Conceptual Understanding

In this unit, the concepts covered in the embedded phase assessments for Phases One, Two, and Three are also incorporated into the final project in Phase Four. As a result, parents can see how their child's conceptual understanding of the relationship between profit, income, and expenses deepens as each student makes spreadsheets in Phase Two and creates graphs in Phase Three. You can also use Lesson 5, "What's My Formula?" Game, as a specific example to demonstrate to parents how an investigation uses technology to introduce algebraic concepts that are an essential foundation for the study of algebra in high school.

Mathematical Processes

Problem solving and mathematical communication occur regularly in daily lessons. The final project is ideal for showing parents the nature of the problem-solving and mathematical communication processes in which their child is engaged. As students use technology to analyze businesses in a real-world setting, they are also thinking logically and using mathematical reasoning to pose a series of what-if questions and gather data to test their recommendations. You may want to invite parents to visit the class and ask students to demonstrate their completed final projects on the computer.

LESSON 4

Investigate Profit on a Spreadsheet

1. row 5; row 3

2. column F; column C; column D

3. cell G6; cell B4

Explore What-If Questions on a Spreadsheet

1.

	No. Sold	Profit
Potato chips	1,200	$180.00
Chocolate chip cookies	1,500	$375.00
Popcorn	1,600	$240.00
Total profit		$795.00

2.

	No. Sold	Profit
Potato chips	300	$45.00
Chocolate chip cookies	375	$93.75
Popcorn	400	$60.00
Total profit		$198.75

3.

	Expenses	Profit
Potato chips	$180.00	$0.00
Chocolate chip cookies	$225.00	$75.00
Popcorn	$240.00	$0.00
Total profit		$75.00

4.

	No. Sold	Profit
Potato chips	0	−$90.00
Chocolate chip cookies	750	$187.50
Popcorn	800	$120.00
Total profit		$217.50

5.

	Price	Profit
Potato chips	$0.40	$150.00
Chocolate chip cookies	$0.50	$262.50
Popcorn	$0.40	$200.00
Total profit		$612.50

6.

	Price	Expenses	Profit
Potato chips	$0.45	$180.00	$90.00
Chocolate chip cookies	$0.55	$225.00	$187.50
Popcorn	$0.45	$240.00	$120.00
Total profit			$397.50

REPRODUCIBLE 17

Finding Profit Using a Calculator

1.

Booth	No. Sold	Price	Income	Cost per Item	Expenses	Profit
Potato chips	175	$ 0.30	$ 52.50	$ 0.15	$ 26.25	$ 26.25
Chocolate chip cookies	250	$ 0.30	$ 75.00	$ 0.15	$ 37.50	$ 37.50
Popcorn	400	$ 0.30	$120.00	$ 0.15	$ 60.00	$ 60.00
Totals			$		$	$123.75

2.

Booth	No. Sold	Price	Income	Cost per Item	Expenses	Profit
Potato chips	20	$ 0.50	$ 10.00	$ 0.15	$ 3.00	$ 7.00
Chocolate chip cookies	800	$ 0.50	$400.00	$ 0.15	$120.00	$280.00
Popcorn	5	$ 0.60	$ 3.00	$ 0.15	$ 0.75	$ 2.25
Totals			$		$	$289.25

3.

Booth	No. Sold	Price	Income	Cost per Item	Expenses	Profit
Potato chips	175	$ 0.50	$ 87.50	$ 0.25	$ 43.75	$ 43.75
Chocolate chip cookies	250	$ 0.50	$125.00	$ 0.25	$ 62.50	$ 62.50
Popcorn	400	$ 0.60	$240.00	$ 0.25	$100.00	$140.00
Totals			$		$	$246.25

LESSON 5

Write Formulas in Spreadsheet Notation

1. D3, Income for Potato Chips Booth

2. G4, Profit for Chocolate Chip Cookies Booth

3. =B5*C5; =D4–F4; =G3+G4+G5

ADDITIONAL SOLUTIONS

LESSON 5: REPRODUCIBLE R18

Getting to 25

Other solutions are possible.

1. B1=10; C2=3; D3=13. To get to 25: =D3+12

2. B1=3; C4=9; D3=27. To get to 25: = D3−2

3. B2=36; B4=24; C1=8; D3=32. To get to 25: =D3−7

4. D1=14; B3=11.5; B1=15; C2=3; D3=12. To get to 25: =D3+13

5. C1=5.1; A4=19.8; D2=19.3; D3=24.3. To get to 25: =D3+.7

6. C3=$\frac{1}{2}$; B2=$\frac{1}{4}$; A1=5; D3=2$\frac{1}{2}$. To get to 25: =D3+22$\frac{1}{2}$

7. A3=27.6; A1=19.7; B2=9.85; D3=29.5. To get to 25: =D3−4.5

8. C1=20; A4=40; B3=20; D3=29. To get to 25: =D3−4

LESSON 8: REPRODUCIBLE R21

Tee-Time's Profits

1. October; Explanations will vary.

2. December; Explanations will vary.

3. September; Explanations will vary.

4. November; Explanations will vary.

5. January; Explanations will vary.

6. Answers will vary.

7. point at intersection of April and $2,000

8. point at intersection of May and $1,000

LESSON 8

Homework

2.

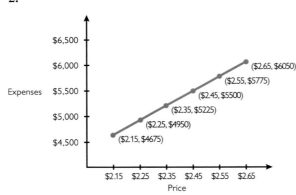

3.

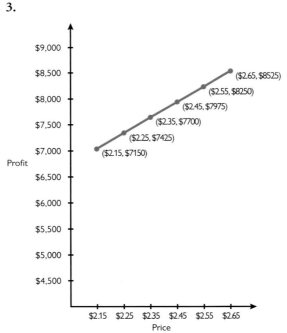

8.

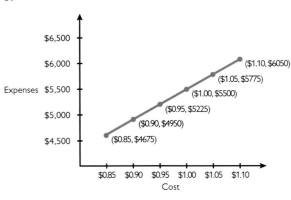

9.

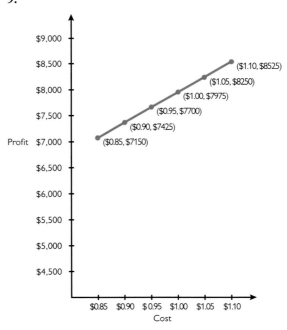

Make Qualitative Graphs

Possible solution is shown.

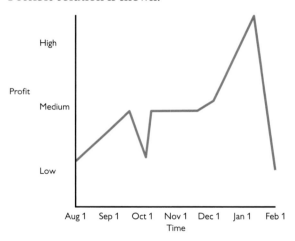

Create the Missing Graphs

Month 1

Income and expenses are the same to start with, so profit begins at 0. Since expenses stay constant, and income increases, profit mirrors income and also increases at the same rate. This is direct variation. In general, if expenses are constant, profit and income will mirror each other.

Month 2

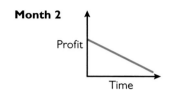

Now income stays constant, while expenses increase. The difference between income and expenses (which is profit) becomes less and less, so profit decreases. In general, if income remains constant, profit will do the opposite of expenses.

Month 3

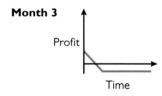

Income starts out greater than expenses and drops to a constant that is less than expenses. This causes the difference (profit) to lessen until it is zero (the point at which income and expenses are equal). When expenses exceed income profit is negative.

Month 4

Income remains constant, while expenses decrease, so inversely, profits increase. Expenses start at a point greater than income so profit is negative. When income and expenses are equal, profit is 0. Then income exceeds expenses, so profit is positive.

Month 5

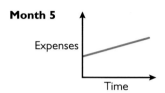

Both income and profit increase. At first, this may lead students to think that expenses are constant, but this is not true. Profit increases more slowly than income. The difference between income and expenses, therefore, is slowly increasing. This means expenses are increasing also, but more slowly than income, causing the difference to widen or increase.

Month 6

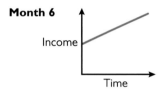

Profits increase rather quickly. This would happen most quickly when income increases and expenses decrease, causing the difference between them to widen or increase quickly. So income increases, but not as quickly as the profit graph.

Month 7

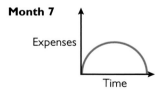

The profit graph shows a deep dip in the middle. This indicates the difference between income and expenses is least here, and greatest at the ends. This means expenses start low, increase in the middle, and then decrease again at the end.

REPRODUCIBLE R24

Predicting Profits

Part I

Possible solutions are:

1. Income down, expenses down, profit same

2. Income up, expenses up, profit same

3. Income same, expenses up, profit down.

4. Income same, expenses down, profit up

5. Income up, expenses same, profit up

6–8. Answers will vary.

Part II

Possible solutions are:

1. A   2. A   3. D or E

4. B or C   5. B or C

Explanations will vary.

Part III

Answers will vary.

LESSON 11

Homework

1.

	A	B	C	D	E	F	G
1	Item	Number Sold	Price	Income	Cost per Item	Expenses	Profit
2	Tape	300	$1.45	$435.00	$0.55	$165.00	$ 270.00
3	Box of Staples	450	$1.85	$832.50	$0.55	$247.50	$ 585.00
4	Binder	125	$2.50	$312.50	$1.45	$181.25	$ 131.25
5	Box of Paper Clips	182	$1.75	$318.50	$0.60	$109.20	$ 209.30
6	Colored Pencils	74	$3.40	$251.60	$0.85	$ 62.90	$ 188.70
7	Totals	1,131					$1384.25

6. Graph C

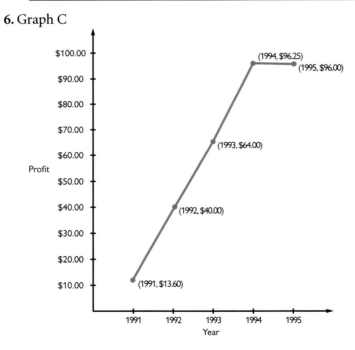

Homework

Solutions: Lesson 1

1. Income is c; expenses are a, b, and d.
2. Answers will vary depending on stores and different preferences.
3. Possible answers are: What will the expenses be and how many people are expected to visit the booth?
4. If income exceeds expenses. In other words, if there is a profit.
5. The profit would increase by $10.
6. Income is like deposits; expenses are like withdrawals. Profit is like account balance because profit is the difference between income and expenses, and account balance is the difference between deposits and withdrawals.
7. $225.42

To Sell or Not to Sell Gourmet Hot Dogs

Applying Skills

1. Make two columns. Label one column "Expenses" and the other "Income." Put the following business situations for Newburger's Seasoned Hot Dog Booth under the appropriate column.

   a. Paid for photocopying expenses to make flyers for advertising.
   b. Purchased food from Harry and Don's Hot Dog Distributing Company.
   c. Sold 20 hot dogs to a family for a cookout.
   d. Purchased relish, ketchup, and mustard from a supermarket.

2. As owner of Anne's Amorphous Shoe Store, decide which option listed below (A, B, or C) you will choose to advertise your upcoming shoe sale and explain why. Use the information in the table shown to make your decision. You will need to call your local copying center and newspaper to get more information.

Option	Type of Advertising	How Many People Will Know About Sale	Cost
A	100 flyers	500	call for photocopying cost
B	half-page newspaper advertisement	1,200	call for newspaper advertising costs
C	sign in window	200	$5.00

Extending Concepts

3. If you were the owner of Newburger's Seasoned Hot Dog Booth, what information would you need to decide how much you should charge the customer for each hot dog?

4. How would you know if your hot dog booth was successful?

5. If Newburger's Seasoned Hot Dog Booth's income increased by $10 and its expenses remained the same, what would happen to the hot dog booth's profit?

Making Connections

The relationship between income, expenses, and profit is similar to the relationship between deposits, withdrawals, and account balance. Example: I have $300 in the bank and deposit $200. If I withdraw $50, my account balance would be $450.

Transaction Statement for: _____ Account #: 453565233			
Date	Transaction Type	Amount	Account Balance
04/27/96	Open Account	$300.00	$300.00
04/28/96	Deposit	$200.00	$500.00
05/01/96	Withdrawal	$50.00	$450.00

6. Explain how deposit, withdrawal, and account balance are related to income, expenses, and profit.

7. Calculate the final account balance after examining the Transaction Statement for Account #7896543.

Transaction Statement for: _____ Account #: 7896543		
Account balance before first transaction on this statement: $525.00		
Date	Transaction Type	Amount
06/01/96	Withdrawal	$234.65
06/03/96	Withdrawal	$92.75
06/12/96	Deposit	$253.92
06/12/96	Withdrawal	$210.35
06/18/96	Withdrawal	$15.75

A Food Booth at a School Fair

Applying Skills

Last April, it cost Newburger's Seasoned Hot Dog Booth $50 to buy a dozen jumbo packages of hot dogs and rolls from Harry and Don's Hot Dog Distributing Company. Each jumbo package contains 10 hot dogs and 10 rolls.

1. As the manager of Newburger's Seasoned Hot Dog Booth, you would like to find out how profit increases when the price of each hot dog increases. Use the information above to help you make a table as shown and fill it in.

Cost of Hot Dog on a Roll	Price of Hot Dog on a Roll	Profit from Selling 1 Hot Dog on a Roll
	$0.50	
	$0.75	
	$1.00	
	$1.25	

2. How much should you sell each hot dog for if you would like to break even?

3. If it now costs $75 to buy a dozen jumbo packages of hot dogs and rolls, how much would you sell the hot dogs for if you would like Newburger's Seasoned Hot Dog Booth to break even?

Unfortunately, it rained during the Fall Fair this year so not as many people showed up at Newburger's Seasoned Hot Dog Booth. As a result, the hot dog booth sold only 300 hot dogs instead of the expected 600 hot dogs. The owner, Mr. Newburger, bought 600 hot dogs for $0.55 each and sold them for $2.00 each.

4. How much profit would Mr. Newburger have made if he had sold 600 hot dogs?

5. How much profit did Mr. Newburger make selling 300 hot dogs?

6. How much expected profit did Mr. Newburger lose because of the rain?

Extending Concepts

7. In general, if income decreases by half and expenses remain the same, does that mean that profit will decrease by half?

8. Give an example of a situation where income is cut in half, expenses are cut in half, and profit is cut in half. Include numbers in your example.

9. One way to calculate the profit from selling 100 soccer balls is to subtract the total expenses of buying the soccer balls from the total income from selling the soccer balls. If you subtract the cost of buying one soccer ball from the price of selling one soccer ball and then multiply by 100, is this another way to calculate the correct profit? If so, why does this work? Will it always work?

Making Connections

10. Use the following table to decide from which bank you would like to obtain a one-year, $3,000 loan. Explain why. Support your decision with calculations. If you are not sure about how to calculate interest, ask your teacher or parent.

Name of Bank	Length of Loan	Interest Rate	Service Fee
Alligator Bank	1 year	2.9%	$200
Barracuda Bank	1 year	3.2%	none

Solutions: Lesson 2

1.

Cost of Hot Dog on a Roll	Price of Hot Dog on a Roll	Profit from Selling 1 Hot Dog on a Roll
$0.42	$0.50	$0.08
$0.42	$0.75	$0.33
$0.42	$1.00	$0.58
$0.42	$1.25	$0.83

2. $0.42   **3.** $0.63

4. $870.00   **5.** $270.00

6. $600.00

7. No, it will never happen, unless expenses are zero. For example, if Income = 10 and Expenses = 4, then Profit is 6. If Income = 5 and Expenses = 4, then Profit is 1.

8. Possible answer is: If Income = 20 and Expenses = 10, then Profit is 10. If Income = 10 and Expenses = 5, then Profit is 5.

9. Yes, it will always work because of the distributive property.

10. Barracuda Bank

$3,000 × 2.9% = $87; $87 + $200 = $287

$3,000 × 3.2% = $96

Solutions: Lesson 3

1. $155
2. $250
3. $13,000
4. increase price; increase number sold
5. $30 per week

6.

Type of Hot Dog	Income	Expenses	Profit
Plain	$237.60	$30.00	$207.60
Gourmet	$168.00	$55.00	$113.00

7. Check students' reasoning. Possible answer: Plain hot dogs, because she sold 88% of all she bought at a price 9 times the cost. She sold only 80% of the gourmet hot dogs at about 3.8 times the cost.

8. One possible answer is to increase price of gourmet hot dogs or decrease price of plain hot dogs.

9. Possible answers are to look at the data from previous sales of hot dogs and study the prospective customer base.

10. overestimating by 24 plain hot dogs

11. Answers will vary, but in effect if the price is too high, then people won't buy the hot dogs.

What-If Questions for the Food Booth

Applying Skills

Imagine that you are a consultant to Bernie's Burger Restaurant and have the following information:

Bernie's Burger Restaurant

Income and Expense Report

INCOME $250 per week
EXPENSES $95 per week

1. What is Bernie's Burger Restaurant's profit per week?

2. If you give the restaurant advice that will double its income, how much more profit will it make per week?

3. If the restaurant's income is doubled, how much more profit will they make in a year?

4. Name two ways income can be increased.

5. If expenses increase $30 per week, how much does income need to increase so that profit does not change?

A local businesswoman, Ann Tagoni, opened a hot dog booth to compete with Newburger's Seasoned Hot Dog Booth. Ms. Tagoni's records for one day of selling hot dogs at the Fall Fair are shown in the table below.

Type of Hot Dog	Number Bought	Cost	Number Sold	Price
Plain	200	$0.15	176	$1.35
Gourmet	100	$0.55	80	$2.10

6. Make a table like the one shown below and fill it in using the information from the Table of Ms. Tagoni's Records.

Type of Hot Dog	Income	Expenses	Profit
Plain			
Gourmet			

7. If Ann Tagoni wanted to make the most profit, should she sell plain or gourmet hot dogs?

Extending Concepts

8. Explain two changes in the entries in the Table of Ms. Tagoni's Records that she could make so that the profit from selling plain and gourmet hot dogs would be equal.

9. If you were the person in charge of buying hot dogs for Ann Tagoni's hot dog stand, how would you determine how many hot dogs to buy so that you do not buy too many?

10. Which is more profitable: overestimating by 24 plain hot dogs like Ms. Tagoni did, or underestimating by 24 plain hot dogs and buying only 152, all of which sold?

Writing

11. One of Ann Tagoni's employees thinks that the price of gourmet hot dogs should be a lot higher. Write about what would happen if Ms. Tagoni raised the price of gourmet hot dogs really high and what effect that would have on profit.

What-If Questions on Spreadsheets

Applying Skills

Use the following information about Bodacious Bicycles for items 1–4.

Information for Making the Spreadsheet

- The store sells four brands of bicycles at the following prices:

  Trek $225
  KTS $275
  Bianchi $285
  Gary Fisher $300

- This is a list of the bicycles from lowest to highest cost to the store: Trek, KTS, Bianchi, and Gary Fisher.

- It costs the store $110 to buy a Trek bicycle from the manufacturing company. The cost of each bike increases by $20.

- In 1996, the store sold 300 Treks, 150 KTS's, 125 Bianchis, and 80 Gary Fishers.

1. Make a spreadsheet with these column headings: Brand of Bicycle, Number Sold, Price, Income, Cost, Expenses, and Profit. Label the columns with letters and rows with numbers. Fill in the data in your spreadsheet using the information given.

2. What if the store sold 20 fewer Trek bicycles and increased the number of KTS bicycles sold by 20 bicycles? Tell what the total profit would be.

3. What if each of the Gary Fisher bicycles had been sold for $35 more than the price shown? Tell what the store's new total profit from the sales of all of its bicycles would be. Which cells did you add to find the answer?

4. What if the store owner wanted the total profit to be $501 more and he could only change the price of Trek bicycles? Figure out how much he would have to charge for Trek bicycles.

Extending Concepts

Use the spreadsheet shown of Linton's Lemon Shop's business for April to complete items 5–6.

	A	B	C	D	E	F	G
1	Item	Number Sold	Price	Income	Cost per Item	Expenses	Profit
2							
3	Lemons	15,000	$0.18	$2,700.00	$0.05	$750.00	$1,950.00

5. If cost doubled, how many cells will change? Which cell(s) will change?

6. If cost doubled and price doubled, what will the new profit be?

Writing

7. Write at least three what-if questions for Bodacious Bicycles. Tell how each question would affect their profit, income, and expenses.

Homework

Solutions: Lesson 4

1.

	A	B	C	D	E	F	G
1	Brand	Number Sold	Price	Income	Cost	Expenses	Profit
2	Trek	300	$225	$67,500	$110	$33,000	$34,500
3	KTS	150	$275	$41,250	$130	$19,500	$21,750
4	Bianchi	125	$285	$35,625	$150	$18,750	$16,875
5	Gary Fisher	80	$300	$24,000	$170	$13,600	$10,400
6	Total						$83,525

2. $84,125

3. $86,325; cells G2+G3+G4+G5

4. $226.67

5. 3 cells, E3, F3, G3

6. $3,900

7. Answers will vary.

Solutions: Lesson 5

1. D2
2. G4
3. F5
4. G7
5. $=$B2*E2
6. $=$D5$-$F5
7. $=$G2+G3+G4+G5+G6
8. cells D4, G4, and G7
9. $=$F2+F3+F4+F5+F6; put in F7
10. $=$B5*C5 $-$ B5*D5
11. $=$B2*C2$-$B2*E2+B3*C3$-$B3*E3+B4*C4$-$B4*E4
    +B5*C5$-$B5*E5+B6*C6$-$B6*E6
    Another possibility:
    $=$D2$-$F2+D3$-$F3+D4$-$F4+D5$-$F5+D6$-$F6
12. No, because that cell is not an input cell. It is a cell that is dependent on other information from cells B3 and E3 because F3$=$B3*E3.
13. Answers will vary, but possibilities are: change number sold, cost, or price. If total profit was calculated by a spreadsheet formula, the profit should change accordingly.
14. Explanations will vary.

	A	B	C	D	E	F	G
1	Student Name	Quiz 1	Quiz 2	Quiz 3	Test 1	Test 2	Test 3
2	Michael	90	85	100	95	90	80

H	I
Quiz Average	Test Average
=(B2+C2+D2)/3	=(E2+F2+G2)/3

"What's My Formula?" Game

Applying Skills

A spreadsheet of Caryn's Creative Card Store's business for the month of March is shown.

	A	B	C	D	E	F	G
1	Type of Card	Number Sold	Price	Income	Cost per Item	Expenses	Profit
2	Blank	300	$1.65	$495.00	$0.75	$225.00	$270.00
3	Birthday	450	$2.15	$967.50	$0.85	$382.50	$585.00
4	Anniversary	125	$1.90	$237.50	$0.85	$106.25	$131.25
5	Thank you	120	$1.65	$198.00	$0.60	$72.00	$126.00
6	Get well	80	$1.40	$112.00	$0.55	$44.00	$68.00
7	Total						$1,180.25

1. What cell would have the formula $=$B2*C2?

2. What cell would have the formula $=$D4$-$F4?

3. What cell would have the formula $=$B5*E5?

4. Which cell has a spreadsheet formula that uses more than two different cells?

5. Write the formula for cell F2.

6. Write the formula for cell G5.

7. Write the formula for cell G7.

8. If the information in cell C4 changes, which cells will also change?

9. Write a spreadsheet formula that could make the calculation for the total expenses. In what new cell would you put this formula?

Extending Concepts

10. If you decided not to have an income column and expenses column, what would be the formula for cell E5 for Caryn's Creative Card Store spreadsheet?

11. If you decided not to have a column for profit, but instead only a cell for total profit, what would be the formula for the Total Profit cell for Caryn's Creative Card Store spreadsheet?

12. If this spreadsheet uses formulas, can you put only a number in cell F3? Explain.

13. Not everyone who uses spreadsheets knows how to write spreadsheet formulas. Mario just computed the expenses, income, and profit on a calculator, then entered them in the spreadsheet instead of using the spreadsheet formulas so the computer can do the computation. If you were looking at a spreadsheet on a computer, how would you be able to determine if the total profit was calculated by a calculator or a spreadsheet formula? (Hint: What if you could change only one cell?)

Making Connections

14. Explain how a teacher could use a spreadsheet to record students' grade information and how it can help save time when computing grade averages. Imagine that you are the teacher. Make a spreadsheet that you would set up which would keep track of information in the most efficient way using these column headings: Student Name, Quiz 1, Quiz 2, Quiz 3, Test 1, Test 2, Test 3, Quiz Average, and Test Average. Make up quiz and test data, and then add formulas to the spreadsheet.

GETTING DOWN TO BUSINESS   HOMEWORK 5
40   © Creative Publications • MathScape

GETTING DOWN TO BUSINESS ASSESSMENT
© Creative Publications • MathScape   **A33**

Double Your Profits?

Applying Skills

A spreadsheet for a simulation of Tobias's Tire Company is shown.

	A	B	C	D	E	F	G
1	Type of Tire	Number Sold	Price	Income	Cost per Item	Expenses	Profit
2	Regular	60	$60.95	$3,657.00	$25.00	$1,500.00	$2,157.00
3	Steel-belted	82	$82.95	$6,801.90	$47.00	$3,854.00	$2,947.90
4	Snow tires	20	$75.95	$1,519.00	$36.00	$720.00	$799.00
5							
6	Total						$5,309.90

1. If you wanted to double the profit of your simulation, which cells might have their values increased?

2. If you wanted to double the profit of your simulation, which cells might have their values decreased?

3. If you wanted the profit to increase but the price of each tire to remain the same, which cells would show changed values?

4. Which cells should have formulas?

5. Suppose someone asked what would happen to the profit if the cost of one type of tire increased by $15. Draw a spreadsheet that shows how you changed the data.

Extending Concepts

6. How could Tobias's Tire Company double its profit, but keep its prices low and therefore keep its customers happy? Explain your answer.

7. If companies want to double profit, which do you think they have more control over, reducing cost or raising price? Explain your reasoning.

Making Connections

The cardiac cycle consists of the contraction and relaxation of the chambers of the heart: the atriums and ventricles.

With each beat of the heart, about 70 mL of blood is pumped into the aorta, the artery that carries blood throughout the body. At a heart rate of 75 beats per minute, 5,250 mL of blood is pumped each minute. This is called the *minute output.*

To find out the length of each cardiac cycle, a scientist divides 60 seconds by the heart rate.

8. Use the facts above to make a spreadsheet like the one shown and fill it in.

	A	B	C
1	Heart Rate	Minute Output (mL)	Length of each Cycle (sec)
2	75	5,250	0.8
3	60		
4	82		
5	65		
6	(your rate)		

9. Find your own pulse and use it to measure your heart rate (how many times your heart beats in 1 minute). Enter information about your heart rate in the three columns of the spreadsheet.

10. Write formulas for columns B and C.

Homework

Solutions: Lesson 6

1. B2, B3, B4, D2, D3, D4, G2, G3, G4, G6

2. E2, E3, E4, F2, F3, F4

3. Answers will vary. Either the B and D columns change to show increased sales or the E and F columns change to show decreased expenses.

4. D2, D3, D4, F2, F3, F4, G2, G3, G4, G6

5. Answers will vary. If, for example, a student raises steel-belted tire cost to $62, F3 will change to $5,084.00, G3 will change to $1,717.90, and G6 will change to $4,673.90.

6. Answers will vary. It must cut expenses or try to sell more tires.

7. raising prices because distributors or manufacturers set the cost of items

8–9.

	A	B	C
1	Heart Rate (beats per minute)	Minute Output (mL)	Length of Each Cycle (sec)
2	75	5,250	0.8
3	60	4,200	1
4	82	5,740	0.73
5	65	4,550	0.92
6	answers will vary	answers will vary	answers will vary

10. Column B: =A2*70; =A3*70; =A4*70; =A5*70
    Column C: =60/A2; =60/A3; =60/A4; =60/A5

Solutions: Lesson 7

1.

	A	B	C
1	Potential Price per Hammer	Number of Hammers Consumers Would Buy at this Price	Potential Income from Hammer Sales
2	$9.00	240	$2,160.00
3	$12.00	216	$2,592.00
4	$17.00	150	$2,550.00
5	$22.00	125	$2,750.00
6	$28.00	98	$2,744.00

2. $4.00   3. $28.00

4–5. Intersection point is ($17, 150). A hammer will sell for $17.

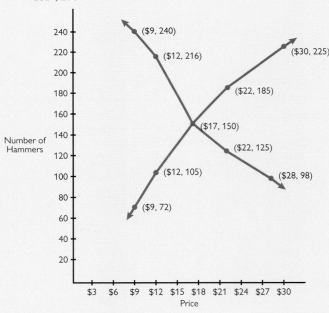

6. One possible answer is:

	A	B	C	D	E
1	Date of Use	Phone Number of Modem	Beginning Time	Ending Time	Amount of Time
2	09/26/96	205 555 0000	10:20	10:48	=D2–C2

How Many Sales at Tee-Time?

Applying Skills

Hank's Hardware makes and sells tools. Use the spreadsheet below to complete items 1–4.

	A	B	C
1	Potential Price per Hammer	Number of Hammers that Consumers Would Buy at This Price	Potential Income from Hammer Sales
2	$9.00	240	
3	$12.00		$2,592.00
4		150	$2,550.00
5	$22.00	125	
6		98	$2,744.00

1. Make a spreadsheet like the one shown for Hank's Hardware and fill in the blank cells of the spreadsheet.

2. If you knew that the profit earned from selling the $12.00 hammers was $1,728.00, what was the cost of buying each hammer?

3. If the cost of hammers increased to $6.25, which price should the hammer be sold for to make the greatest profit?

Extending Concepts

4. Make a graph using the spreadsheet from Hank's Hardware. Graph the number of hammers that would be bought by consumers at this price vs. the potential price of the hammer.

Making Connections

Economists interpret graphs like the one you drew for Hank's Hardware in item 4 along with another graph to determine how much to charge for an item.

The graph you made for Hank's Hardware would be called the *demand curve* because those prices represent what the consumers are willing to pay. In economics, accompanying the demand curve is a supply curve. The *supply curve* is determined by the number of items the manufacturer is willing to produce at a certain price. The *intersection point* of these two curves usually is the price for which the items are sold.

5. The spreadsheet shown indicates the number of hammers Hank is willing to produce at certain prices. Graph the information from this spreadsheet on your graph from item 4. Find the intersection point to determine how much a hammer will sell for.

	Price per Hammer	Number of Hammers the Manufacturer Is Willing to Produce at This Price
1		
2	$9.00	72
3	$12.00	105
4	$17.00	150
5	$22.00	185
6	$30.00	225

6. You are hired as a business consultant by Swish Internet Company, a new business that bills customers for time spent using the Internet. The company would like you to create a spreadsheet to keep track of the time people spend on the Internet. Include the following information in your spreadsheet:

a. phone number of the modem being used

b. beginning time and ending time of use

c. date

d. amount of time spent using the Internet

Make up some data for your spreadsheet and then add formulas to your spreadsheet.

How Much Profit at Tee-Time?

Applying Skills

Caryn's Creative Card Store wants to project the sales of birthday cards in the future. Caryn figures that she will sell approximately 5,500 birthday cards per year. The cost of the cards will increase $0.05 per year so the price she will sell them for will increase by $0.10 per year. Use the data in this table to make graphs and answer questions.

	A	B	C	D	E	F
1	Year	Price of Birthday Cards ($)	Income ($)	Cost of Birthday Cards ($)	Expense ($)	Profit ($)
2	1996	2.15	11,825.00	0.85	4,675.00	7,150.00
3	1997	2.25	12,375.00	0.90	4,950.00	7,425.00
4	1998	2.35	12,925.00	0.95	5,225.00	7,700.00
5	1999	2.45	13,475.00	1.00	5,500.00	7,975.00
6	2000	2.55	14,025.00	1.05	5,775.00	8,250.00
7	2001	2.65	14,575.00	1.10	6,050.00	8,525.00

1. Plot a price vs. income graph.

2. Plot a price vs. expenses graph.

3. Plot a price vs. profit graph.

4. Does the price vs. income graph look similar to the price vs. profit graph? Why or why not?

Use the graphs shown to complete items 5–7.

5. What information does point **A** on the graph give you?

6. What information does point **B** on the graph give you?

7. What information does point **C** on the graph give you?

Use the data from Caryn's Creative Card Store for the years 1996–2001 to complete items 8–9.

8. Plot a cost vs. expenses graph.

9. Plot a cost vs. profit graph.

Extending Concepts

10. Why do your graphs for price vs. expenses and price vs. profit look similar?

11. The price vs. profit graph is different from the price vs. income graph. What do you think has caused this change?

Writing

12. Write a paragraph explaining how graphs and spreadsheets can be related to each other. Be sure to give examples.

Solutions: Lesson 8

1.
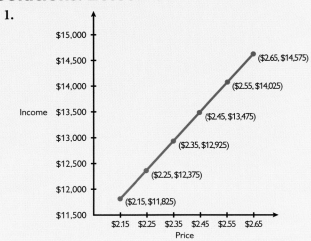

2–3. See Assessment page A26.

4. Yes, because the general trend line of each graph is a straight line, but the income line is steeper because the increments between successive income values are larger than the increments between successive profit values.

5. most profitable price at which to sell item

6. the cost that yields the lowest expenses

7. the price that gives the greatest income

8–9. See Assessment page A26.

10. because both expenses and profit increase in increments of $275 for each successive price.

11. The price vs. profit graph is less steep than the price vs. income graph, since the growth in the successive profit values is reduced by the concurrent growth in expenses.

12. Answers will vary.

Solutions: Lesson 9

1.

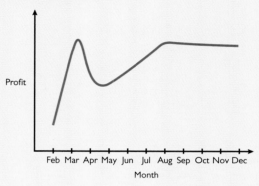

2.

3. Possible answer: Since price decreased, the number sold may have increased.

4. Possible answer: Sellers of fax machines increased price to balance increase in cost.

5. Possible answer: The number sold increased so that the decrease in price did not lead to a decrease in profit.

6. Possible answer: People still want to send hand-written documents so faxes are still important.

7. Possible answer: More people are using the Internet instead of faxes. The number of fax machines sold went down.

8. Possible answer: Number Sold vs. Price; as price increases, the number sold decreases.

9. The trend was an increase, with an overall gain of more than 400 points between 1987 and 1997.

10. Answers will vary. There may be a fall in the stock market, but it will most likely go up again.

Months Later at Tee-Time

Applying Skills

Draw a rough sketch of a profits vs. months graph for each description of these companies.

1. The Contemporary Video Store's March profits doubled from February. April was not as strong, especially since they had a lot of expenses for repairing their store after a severe storm. During the summer months the store righted itself and, by the end of August, its profits were almost the same as those earned in March. The profits remained steady until the end of the year. The company decided to keep prices the same throughout this entire period.

2. Anjali's Antique Store opened its doors in March. Tourist season was just beginning, so Anjali had a great number of customers stop by to buy antiques. Sales were steady throughout April, May, June, and July, but stagnated in the beginning of August. Anjali's business really struggled in September, October, and November when it became cold. Sadly, Anjali had to close her store in December when she could only break even from selling antiques.

Read over the Action and Result columns for Tamika's Telecommunications Store, which sells fax machines. For items **3–7**, write a brief description of why the result occurred at the store. There is more than one possibility.

	Action	Result
3.	Price of faxes decreases.	Profit increases.
4.	Cost of faxes increases.	Profit stays the same.
5.	Price of faxes decreases.	Profit stays the same.
6.	Phone company decreases the cost of using the phone.	Profit stays the same.
7.	Internet increases in popularity.	Profits decrease.

Extending Concepts

8. Identify the labels for each axis of this graph. Explain your labels using what you have learned about profit, income, and expenses.

Making Connections

The status of the Standard and Poor's 500 Index, or S&P 500 as it is commonly referred to, is a good measuring tool to see how the New York Stock Exchange is performing.

9. Look at the graph that shows the general trend of the S&P 500 Index and describe what has occurred in the past ten years.

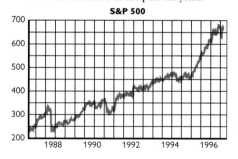

10. Make a prediction of how you think the S&P 500 Index will perform in the next ten years by sketching a graph like the one provided. Explain your reasoning.

North Mall Cinema's Project

Applying Skills

Linton's Lemon Shop

	A	B	C	D	E	F	G	H
1	Month	Item	Number Sold	Price	Income	Cost per Item	Expenses	Profit
2	April	Lemons	15,000	$0.18			$750.00	$1,950.00
3	May	Lemons	13,200		$2,508.00	$0.06		

Marty and Margie's Lemon Shop

	A	B	C	D	E	F	G	H
1	Month	Item	Number Sold	Price	Income	Cost per Item	Expenses	Profit
2	April	Lemons	8,000	$0.28			$800.00	$1,440.00
3	May	Lemons		$0.25	$2,995.00	$0.11		

Linton's Lemon Shop has a new competitor, Marty and Margie's Lemon Shop, which sells organically grown lemons. Organic lemons are more yellow and stay fresh longer, but they are more expensive. Above is a comparison of business for the months of April and May between Linton's Lemon Shop and Marty and Margie's Lemon Shop.

1. Make two spreadsheets as shown and fill in the blanks in the two spreadsheets.

2. Explain which shop is doing better and why.

Extending Concepts

The Bridge, a store specializing in children's ski clothes, has just opened.

3. Put the following situations in order, based on which you think has the greatest effect on The Bridge's profits: weather; hours store is open; cost of items in the store; price of items in the store; month; salary of employees; size of store; number of families living in the area; and how near the store is to the ski slopes. The situation which will have the greatest effect should be listed first, followed by the rest in descending order.

4. Describe the situations that The Bridge can and cannot control.

Making Connections

5. Using the information below, design a spreadsheet that would keep track of items, cost, and price, and calculate total profit. Include the data given and add formulas.

Item	Cost ($)	Price ($)
Soda	1.69	2.39
Shaving cream	1.15	2.19
Tomato sauce	2.09	4.99
Carrots	0.54	1.22
Toothpaste	0.89	1.76
Pasta	3.21	4.56
Beans	1.41	2.53
Rice	0.99	1.47

Solutions: Lesson 10

1.

Linton's Lemon Shop

	A	B	C	D	E	F	G	H
1	Month	Item	No. Sold	Price	Income	Cost/ Item	Expenses	Profit
2	April	Lemons	15,000	$0.18	$2,700.00	$0.05	$750.00	$1,950.00
3	May	Lemons	13,200	$0.19	$2,508.00	$0.06	$792.00	$1,716.00

Marty and Margie's Lemon Shop

	A	B	C	D	E	F	G	H
1	Month	Item	No. Sold	Price	Income	Cost/ Item	Expenses	Profit
2	April	Lemons	8,000	$0.28	$2,240.00	$0.10	$800.00	$1,440.00
3	May	Lemons	11,980	$0.25	$2,995.00	$0.11	$1,317.80	$1,677.20

2. Linton's Lemon Shop is doing better. Its profit is $3,666.00 versus Marty and Margie's Lemon Shop which has a profit of $3,117.20

3. Answers will vary.

4. The Bridge can control: hours open, price of items, salary, and size of store. The Bridge cannot control: weather, cost of items in the store, month, number of families living in the area, and how near the store is to the ski slopes.

5.

	A	B	C	D	E
1	Name of Item	Quantity	Cost per Item	Price per Item	Profit
2	Soda		$1.69	$2.39	=B2*(D2−C2)
3	Shaving cream		$1.15	$2.19	=B3*(D3−C3)
4	Tomato sauce		$2.09	$4.99	=B4*(D4−C4)
5	Carrots		$0.54	$1.22	=B5*(D5−C5)
6	Toothpaste		$0.89	$1.76	=B6*(D6−C6)
7	Pasta		$3.21	$4.56	=B7*(D7−C7)
8	Beans		$1.41	$2.53	=B8*(D8−C8)
9	Rice		$0.99	$1.47	=B9*(D9−C9)
10	Total profit				=E2+E3+E4+E5+ E6+E7+E8+E9

Solutions: Lesson 11

1. See Assessment page A28.
2. Profit would increase by $510 to $1,894.25.
3. $2.05
4. Total profit would increase by $401.25.
5.

	A	B	C	D	E	F	G
1	Year	Number Sold	Price	Income	Cost per Item	Expenses	Profit
2	1991	136 =D2/C2	$1.25	$170.00 =B2*C2	$1.15	$156.40 =B2*E2	$13.60 =D2−F2
3	1992	160 =D3/C3	$1.50	$240.00 =B3*C3	$1.25	$200.00 =B3*E3	$40.00 =D3−F3
4	1993	160 =D4/C4	$1.75	$280.00 =B4*C4	$1.35	$216.00 =B4*E4	$64.00 =D4−F4
5	1994	175 =D5/C5	$2.00	$350.00 =B5*C5	$1.45	$253.75 =B5*E5	$96.25 =D5−F5
6	1995	160 =D6/C6	$2.25	$360.00 =B6*C6	$1.65	$264.00 =B6*E6	$96.00 =D6−F6
7	Total profit						$309.85 =G2+G3 +G4+G5 +G6

Total profit is $309.85.

6. See Assessment page A28.
7. It would indicate larger increases in profit each year.
8. Graph B is close to being a straight line. There would have to be equal increments in expenses each year.

North Mall Cinema's Spreadsheet

Applying Skills

	A	B	C	D	E	F	G
1	Item	Number Sold	Price	Income	Cost per Item	Expenses	Profit
2	Tape	300	$1.45				$270.00
3	Box of staples		$1.85	$832.50			$585.00
4	Binder	125	$2.50		$1.45		
5	Box of paper clips	182		$318.50	$0.60		
6	Colored pencils		$3.40		$0.85		
7	Totals	1,131					

1. Copy the spreadsheet shown and fill in the blanks by using the clues the spreadsheet provides for you.

2. How would the total profit differ if 200 more colored pencils are sold?

3. If the cost of each box of staples increased by $0.20, what would the new price of a box of staples be in order for profit to remain the same?

4. If the price and cost of binders and tape doubled, how would total profit be affected?

Extending Concepts

5. Using these graphs, make a spreadsheet with these column headings: Year, Number Sold, Price, Income, Cost per Item, Expenses, and Profit. Fill in the data and formulas, and find the total profit.

6. Make a graph showing profit vs. year. Title it Graph C.

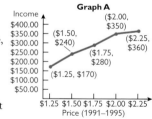

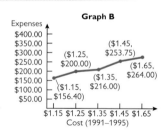

Writing

7. Write a paragraph describing what it would indicate about the relationship between year and profit as the years progressed if Graph A were steeper.

8. Describe the shape of Graph B in a sentence or two. What would have to occur for Graph B to be a straight line?

North Mall Cinema's Report

Applying Skills

The following spreadsheet gives data about the 12 languages spoken by the most people in the world. The spreadsheet identifies the 12 languages and divides the people who speak each language into two categories: native speakers and non-native speakers.

1. Copy the spreadsheet shown and fill in the blanks by using the clues the spreadsheet provides for you. This data is from *The World Almanac and Book of Facts 1996*.

The Principal Languages of the World

	A	B	C	D
1	Language	Number of Native Speakers (millions)	Number of Non-native Speakers (millions)	Total Number of Speakers (millions)
2	Mandarin	844		975
3	English	326		478
4	Hindi		97	437
5	Spanish	339		392
6	Russian	169		284
7	Arabic	190	35	
8	Bengali	193	7	
9	Portuguese	172		184
10	Malay-Indonesian		107	159
11	Japanese	125		126
12	French		52	125
13	German	98		123
14	TOTAL			

2. Write a spreadsheet formula that will calculate the value for D3.

3. Write a spreadsheet formula that will calculate the value for B14.

4. What is the total number of people who speak these 12 languages?

Extending Concepts

Use only these words and mathematical symbols to solve the following problems.

- **Words:** Profit (P), Income (I), Expenses (E), Cost (C), Price (R), Number Sold (S)
- **Symbols:** $+, -, \times, \div, =$

5. If Profit = Income − Expenses, or P = I − E, use words and symbols to write another way of calculating Income.

6. If Profit = Income − Expenses, or P = I − E, use words and symbols to write another way of calculating Expenses.

Making Connections

Below is a spreadsheet about three qualities of animals: gestation, average longevity, and maximum speed. Use this information from *The World Almanac and Book of Facts 1996* to answer the questions below.

	A	B	C	D
1	Animal	Gestation (days)	Average Longevity (years)	Maximum Speed (mph)
2	Grizzly Bear	225	25	30
3	Cat (domestic)	63	12	30
4	White-tailed Deer	201	8	30
5	Giraffe	425	10	32
6	Lion	100	15	50
7	Zebra	365	15	40

7. Write a spreadsheet formula to calculate the average gestation period for the 6 animals.

8. If the maximum speed for a human is 27.89 mph, by how much does it differ from the average maximum speed of the 6 animals?

Homework

Solutions: Lesson 12

1.

	A	B	C	D
1	Language	Number of Native Speakers (millions)	Number of Non-native Speakers	Total Number of Speakers
2	Mandarin	844	131	975
3	English	326	152	478
4	Hindi	340	97	437
5	Spanish	339	53	392
6	Russian	169	115	284
7	Arabic	190	35	225
8	Bengali	193	7	200
9	Portuguese	172	12	184
10	Malay-Indonesian	52	107	159
11	Japanese	125	1	126
12	French	73	52	125
13	German	98	25	123
14	Total			

2. =B3+C3

3. =B2+B3+B4+B5+B6+B7+B8+B9+B10+B11+B12+B13

4. 3,708 million

5. Income = Number Sold*Price; I=S*R

6. Expenses = Number Sold*Cost; E=S*C

7. =(B2+B3+B4+B5+B6+B7)/6

8. 35.33 − 27.89 = 7.44 mph difference

Getting Down to Business
ASSESSMENT CHECKLIST

Name: Period: Date:

Lesson	Assignment Description	Assessment	Notes
Pre-assessment	What math is used to increase profits?		
Lesson 1	To Sell or Not to Sell Gourmet Hot Dogs		
Lesson 2	A Food Booth at a School Fair		
Lesson 3	What-If Questions for the Food Booth		
Phase One Skill Check	Skill Quiz 1 & Homework 1–3		
Lesson 4	What-If Questions on Spreadsheets		
Lesson 5	"What's My Formula?" Game		
Lesson 6	Double Your Profits?		
Phase Two Skill Check	Skill Quiz 2 & Homework 4–6		
Lesson 7	How Many Sales at Tee-Time?		
Lesson 8	How Much Profit at Tee-Time?		
Lesson 9	Months Later at Tee-Time		
Phase Three Skill Check	Skill Quiz 3 & Homework 7–9		
Lesson 10	North Mall Cinema's Project		
Lesson 11	North Mall Cinema's Spreadsheet		
Lesson 12	North Mall Cinema's Report		
Phase Four Skill Check	Skill Quiz 4 & Homework 10–12		
Post-assessment	What math is used to increase profits?		

Comments:

GETTING DOWN TO BUSINESS
© Creative Publications • MathScape

PHASE ONE

Skill Quiz

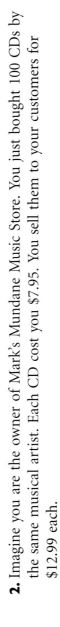

1. Make two columns. Label one column "Expenses," the other "Income." List in the appropriate column these business situations for Little Eddie's Chocolate Treats.

a. sold 100 boxes of chocolate

b. wrote a check to pay for rental of office space from Genuine Realtors

c. paid the salaries of employees working at Little Eddie's

d. purchased refrigerator for storing chocolates

e. paid electricity and phone bill for the month of April

f. received 100 new purchase orders from customers for chocolate delivery

g. paid insurance for the month of April

h. bought new chocolate mixer to replace broken one

2. Imagine you are the owner of Mark's Mundane Music Store. You just bought 100 CDs by the same musical artist. Each CD cost you $7.95. You sell them to your customers for $12.99 each.

a. What is the expense of buying 100 CDs?

b. What is the income from the CDs if you sell all 100 of them?

c. What is the profit from selling all 100 of them?

3. Write an equation that shows the relationship among income, expenses, and profit.

4. In a store window there is a sign that says, "Milk—$1.25." How much do you think it cost the owner of the store to buy the milk?

5. If it costs an artist $20 for supplies to paint a picture on canvas, and the painting sells for $85, how much profit did the artist make after selling the painting?

6. Bronchus's Bookstore bought the bestselling book, *Business Bonanza*, from its book distributor for $6.95 each. Bronchus's sells the book to its customers for $16.95. How much profit does Bronchus's Bookstore make from selling one book? How much profit does the store make from selling 20 books?

7. Can profit be a negative number? If so, describe a situation using numbers to illustrate that the profit in your situation is negative.

PHASE TWO
Skill Quiz

Consuela's Cuisine Food Booth is looking at the food items it sells to determine the profitability of each item. Use the spreadsheet shown to answer questions 1–5.

Consuela's Cuisine Food Booth

	A	B	C	D	E	F	G
1	Item	Number Sold	Price	Income	Cost per Item	Expenses	Profit
2							
3	Paella	200	$3.75	$750.00	$1.35	$270.00	$480.00
4	Rice	325	$1.25	$406.25	$0.15	$48.75	$357.50
5	Tamales	95	$2.75	$261.25	$1.10	$104.50	$156.75
6							
7	Totals						$994.25

1. Name the column that tells about price.
2. Name the cell that tells about paella expenses.
3. Which two cells would you multiply together to find the income from tamales?
4. How much profit was made from all of the items?
5. Which cells were added together to calculate the information in cell G7?

Use the spreadsheet shown about Pedro's Paper Company to answer questions 6–8.

Pedro's Paper Company—November

	A	B	C	D	E	F	G
1	Type of Paper	Number of Sheets	Price per Sheet	Income	Cost per Sheet	Expenses	Profit
2	White	89,000	$0.07	$6,230.00	$0.03	$2,670.00	$3,560.00
3	Colored	62,000	$0.12	$7,440.00	$0.05	$3,100.00	$4,340.00
4	Card stock	15,000	$0.20	$3,000.00	$0.11	$1,650.00	$1,350.00
5							
6	Total						$9,250.00

6. How were the numbers in column F calculated? What formula would appear in cell F4?
7. What recommendations would you make to Pedro's Paper Company for doubling profit?
8. What data in the spreadsheet supports your recommendations?

PHASE THREE
Skill Quiz

A local boat shop, Vincent's Vessels, researched consumers' attitudes toward buying toy boats at different prices. A spreadsheet showing the information is shown. Use the spreadsheet to answer questions 1–2.

	A Price of Toy Boat	B Number of People Who Want to Buy Toy Boat at This Price	C Income from the Sale of Toy Boat
1			
2	$8.95	1,000	$
3	$14.95	680	$
4	$32.95	250	$

1. At which price will the most people buy the toy boat?

2. Make a spreadsheet like the one shown and fill in the Income column. At which price is the most income earned?

3. Look at the Price vs. Income graph and describe in your own words what the graph is showing.

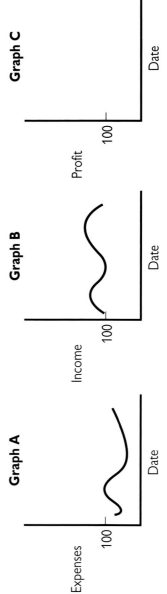

For questions 4–7 below, choose one or more of these kinds of graphs:

a. Price vs. Income   **b.** Price vs. Cost   **c.** Price vs. Profit

4. If you would like to know what happens to income as price increases, which graph would be most beneficial to analyze? Briefly explain your choice.

5. If you would like to know what the most profitable price to charge is, which graph would be most beneficial to analyze? Briefly explain your choice.

6. If you would like to know what happens to income as cost increases, which two graphs could be analyzed together? Briefly explain your choice.

7. If you would like to know what happens to profit as cost increases, which two graphs could be analyzed together? Briefly explain your choice.

8. Look at Graph A and Graph B. Use these two graphs to sketch and complete Graph C.

PHASE FOUR
Skill Quiz

1. What are two ways to double your profit if your income is $80 and your expenses are $52?

2. What are four ways to double your profit if you sell 100 cookies for $0.95 each and it costs $0.15 to make each cookie?

3. Presently, your income is two times as large as your expenses. In the future, if expenses double, what does your income have to do in order for profit to double? Give an example to help explain your reasoning.

4. Presently, your income is two times as large as your expenses. In the future, if expenses double, what does your income have to do in order for profit to remain the same? Give an example to help explain your reasoning.

5. Presently, your income is three times as large as your expenses. In the future, if income doubles, what do your expenses have to do in order for profits to double? Give an example to help explain your reasoning.

6. If income increases and expenses stay the same, what will profit do? Give an example to help explain your reasoning.

7. If income stays the same and expenses increase, what will profit do? Give an example to help explain your reasoning.

8. Is this a true equation: Profit + Expenses = Income? Explain the equation in words. Then write a different equation using profit, income, and expenses. Make sure it is true.

The Stock Management Company in your hometown has heard about spreadsheets and would like to create a spreadsheet that would calculate profits. They have made the following headings for their spreadsheet, but cannot figure out how to write formulas for specific columns. Please help them by answering questions 9–11 that they have posed.

	A	B	C	D	E	F	G	H
1	Name of Stock	Number of Shares Owned	Date Shares Bought	Price of Share when Bought	Date Shares Sold	Price of Share when Sold	Net Difference in Price of Share	Profit From Shares Before Taxes
2	SMWQ	2,000	07/05/94	$14\frac{1}{8}$	04/28/96	$22\frac{5}{8}$	$8\frac{1}{2}$	$17,000.00

9. What is the spreadsheet formula for cell G2?

10. What is the spreadsheet formula for cell H2?

11. There is a 28% tax on profits from shares. If you created a Column I with the heading "Profits After Taxes," what would be the spreadsheet formula for cell I2?

Student Assessment Criteria

PHASE ONE

Does my work show that I can...

- list examples of income and expenses for my food booth?

- calculate profit and income with no major math errors, and describe the steps I use?

- calculate how changing income and/or expenses will affect profit?

PHASE TWO

Does my work show that I can...

- create a spreadsheet that meets the requirements of the assignment?

- write formulas correctly in spreadsheet notation, and explain when and where to use them?

- write three what-if questions and clearly explain the meaning of the questions?

PHASE THREE

Does my work show that I can...

- create two or three sets of profit, income, and expense graphs?

- explain the three graphs in a way that shows I understand the relationship among profit, income, and expenses?

PHASE FOUR

Does my work show that I can...

- create an accurate and well-organized spreadsheet with formulas that shows income, expenses, and profit?

- ask what-if questions that relate to the spreadsheet?

- write clear recommendations and explain how each recommendation will make profits increase?

Dear Family,

Our class will soon be starting a new mathematics unit called *Getting Down to Business: Functions and Spreadsheets*. The unit focuses on key topics in functions and technology that have been recommended for middle school students by the National Council of Teachers of Mathematics. It also provides opportunities for students to apply and extend their knowledge of graphs and data analysis.

Throughout the unit, students explore the mathematics related to the basic equation of business: Profit = Income − Expenses. Students examine this function through different studies of fictitious businesses, and learn to use the spreadsheet to explore this function. In addition, they relate data from graphs and from spreadsheets to make recommendations to the businesses.

Here are some of the questions students will investigate:

- What kinds of decisions will you make as you simulate running a business? How can you use mathematics to help you make decisions about your business?

- What are the relationships among profit, income, and expenses?

- What is a spreadsheet for? How can you use it as a problem-solving tool?

- How can you create a spreadsheet that will help you explore ways to increase a business's profits?

- How do graphs help you understand functions?

- What kind of recommendations would you make for a business on the basis of the data you gathered?

You can help your child by discussing some of the examples in the unit. What recommendation is your child making? Why? How would this recommendation help the business increase its profit? Encourage your child to share with you his or her ideas about how businesses use mathematics and technology.

Sincerely,

PART I
The Hot Dog Stand

Setting Up the Food Booth Simulation

Look at your Simulation Recording Sheet. Read each step below and follow the directions. Write your answers to each step on the top of the Simulation Recording Sheet.

1. Choose one of these food items to sell at your booth: potato chips, popcorn, or chocolate chip cookies. You will keep the same food item throughout the simulation.

2. How many items will you buy for your inventory? Last year at the school fair, students who ran food booths sold 150 to 300 items. Sometimes accidents happened, and they lost some of their inventory, so they didn't sell as many items. At other times, large groups of people came to their food booths and they sold much more than they expected.

You have $50 in your budget to buy inventory. Each item costs 15¢. Think carefully about how many items to buy. You do not want to have lots left over, because buying too much will be a waste of your money. But you do not want to run out of items. If you run out, the simulation ends.

3. How much did it cost to buy your beginning inventory?

4. Choose a price to charge for the item you are selling at your booth. You may choose a price from 15¢ to 60¢. Think about this carefully, because once you have decided, you cannot change it during the simulation.

Simulation Recording Sheet

Read Setting Up the Food Booth Simulation to help you answer these questions.

1. Food Item = _____

2. Number of items bought for inventory = _____. Write the number in "Starting amount" at the top of the Number of Inventory column.

3. Total cost of these items = $ _____. Subtract this cost from your $50 and write the amount in "Starting cash" for Turn 1.

4. What price will you charge? $ _____

Number of Inventory	**Turn 1**		
Starting amount: _____	Starting cash:		$ _____
	Income this turn:	$ _____	
	Expenses this turn:	− $ _____	
End of Turn 1: _____	Profit this turn:	= $ _____	
	Total in cash box:		= $ _____
	Turn 2		
	Income this turn:	$ _____	
	Expenses this turn:	− $ _____	
End of Turn 2: _____	Profit this turn:	= $ _____	
	Total in cash box:		+ $ _____ = $ _____
	Turn 3		
	Income this turn:	$ _____	
	Expenses this turn:	− $ _____	
End of Turn 3: _____	Profit this turn:	= $ _____	
	Total in cash box:		+ $ _____ = $ _____
	Turn 4		
	Income this turn:	$ _____	
	Expenses this turn:	− $ _____	
End of Turn 4: _____	Profit this turn:	= $ _____	
	Total in cash box:		+ $ _____ = $ _____
	Turn 5		
	Income this turn:	$ _____	
	Expenses this turn:	− $ _____	
End of Turn 5: _____	Profit this turn:	= $ _____	
	Total in cash box:		+ $ _____ = $ _____
	Turn 6		
	Income this turn:	$ _____	
	Expenses this turn:	− $ _____	
End of Turn 6: _____	Profit this turn:	= $ _____	
	Total in cash box:		+ $ _____ = $ _____

Deduct the starting amount given to you by Student Council: − $50.00

Final Profit = $ _____

Income Results

If you roll		this happens
2	AND	The Hiking Club has just finished a 6-mile hike, and they need something salty. If you sell potato chips, you sell 35 additional items.
3	AND	People don't want to pay high prices. If your price is 60¢, you sell only 10 items this turn.
4	AND	Someone stumbles and knocks over your boxes of food items. You lose $\frac{1}{10}$ of your inventory.
5	AND	Another food booth selling your item opens near you, charging low prices. If your price is more than 50¢, you sell only 13 items this turn.
6	AND	Some people bring a dog to your booth. While they are talking to some friends, the dog eats $\frac{1}{10}$ of your inventory.
7	AND	People are trying to save money at the fair. If your price is more than 45¢, you sell only 10 items this turn.
8	AND	People don't want to pay high prices. If your price is 55¢ or more, you sell only 10 items this turn.
9	AND	The computer club loves food with "chips!" If you sell chocolate chip cookies, you sell 30 additional items.
10	AND	Captain Kangaroo's Nursery School kids come to the popcorn booth for their snack. If you sell popcorn, you sell 28 additional items.
11	AND	People are trying to save money at the fair. If your price is more than 40¢, you sell only 10 items this turn.
12	AND	People don't want to pay high prices. If your price is 55¢ or more, you sell only 12 items this turn.

The table entries "You sell X items." appear in the middle column:

If you roll	(middle column)
2	You sell 32 items.
3	You sell 35 items.
4	You sell 45 items.
5	You sell 42 items.
6	You sell 38 items.
7	You sell 30 items.
8	You sell 37 items.
9	You sell 36 items.
10	You sell 42 items.
11	You sell 40 items.
12	You sell 38 items.

Expense Results

If you roll	this happens
2	You have no expenses this turn! You pay $0.
3	**Make a Choice:** You may pay $10 for flyers to advertise the food booths. Add 10 to what you sell on the next two turns. Or You may ignore this advertising expense.
4	The counter on your booth breaks and you need to fix it. You pay $10 for materials.
5	**Make a Choice:** You may pay $15 to hire someone to help you work at the booth, so you can sell more. If you do, add 10 items each turn until the end of the game. Or Do nothing and have no expenses.
6	**Make a Choice:** You may buy exactly 50 more items to increase your inventory. If so, add 50 to your inventory number and record an expense of $7.50. Or Do nothing and have no expenses this turn.
7	Someone accidentally rips the sign on your booth. You pay $5 to replace it.
8	**Make a Choice:** You may pay $15 to hire someone to help you work at the booth, so you can sell more. If you do, add 10 items each turn until the end of the game. Or Do nothing and have no expenses.
9	You have no expenses this turn! You pay $0.
10	**Make a Choice:** You may pay $10 for flyers to advertise the food booths. Add 10 to what you sell on the next two turns. Or You may ignore this advertising expense.
11	You have no expenses this turn! You pay $0.
12	You decide to buy special decoration for your booth, so that people will notice you. You pay $15 for decorations.

Profit Made by the Food Booths

	A	B	C	D	E	F	G
1							
2	Booth	Number Sold	Price	Income	Cost per Item	Expenses	Profit
3	Potato chips						
4	Chocolate chip cookies						
5	Popcorn						
6	Totals						

© Creative Publications • MathScape
GETTING DOWN TO BUSINESS

Sample Numbers to Start

400	$0.30	$120.00	$0.15	$60.00	$60.00
450	$0.40	$180.00	$0.15	$67.50	$112.50
600	$0.30	$180.00	$0.15	$90.00	$90.00
					$262.50

GETTING DOWN TO BUSINESS
© Creative Publications • MathScape

What If the Booths Sold More?

500	$0.30	$150.00	$0.15	$75.00	$75.00
550	$0.40	$220.00	$0.15	$82.50	$137.50
700	$0.30	$210.00	$0.15	$105.00	$105.00
					$317.50

Finding Profit Using a Calculator

Fill in the table and find the total profit for each question:

1. What if your price is exactly double your cost?

Booth	Number Sold	Price You Charge	Income	Cost to You per Item	Expenses	Profit
Potato chips	175	$	$	$0.15	$	$
Chocolate chip cookies	250	$	$	$0.15	$	$
Popcorn	400	$	$	$0.15	$	$
Totals			$		$	$

2. What if 800 people buy chocolate chip cookies, 20 people buy chips, and 5 people buy popcorn?

Booth	Number Sold	Price You Charge	Income	Cost to You per Item	Expenses	Profit
Potato chips		$0.50	$	$0.15	$	$
Chocolate chip cookies		$0.50	$	$0.15	$	$
Popcorn		$0.60	$	$0.15	$	$
Totals			$		$	$

3. What if each of your 15¢ costs increases by 10¢? Use the Number Sold figures from Table 1.

Booth	Number Sold	Price You Charge	Income	Cost to You per Item	Expenses	Profit
Potato chips		$0.50	$	$	$	$
Chocolate chip cookies		$0.50	$	$	$	$
Popcorn		$0.60	$	$	$	$
Totals			$		$	$

4. Make up your own what-if question. Make a spreadsheet like those shown here and try out your question. Find the total profit.

5. Come up with another what-if question. Make a spreadsheet like those shown here and try out your question. Find the total profit.

6. What is one change you might make as a business owner in item 5 to raise your profit? Explain how your suggestion affects income and expenses.

Getting to 25

Find the answer to each formula. Then write a formula that uses the number in D3 and gives an answer of 25.

Example:

	A	B	C	D
1	3	=A1+9		
2			=B1−2	
3				=C2+6
4				

A1 = 3   B1 = 3 + 9 = 12   C2 = 12 − 2 = 10   D3 = 10 + 6 = 16
To get to 25, you need to add 9 to 16. The spreadsheet formula =D3+9.

To get to 25: =D3+9

1.

	A	B	C	D
1	5	=A1*2		
2			=B1−7	
3				=C2+10
4				

To get to 25: _____

2.

	A	B	C	D
1		=A2/10		
2	30			
3			=B1*B1	
4				=C4*3

To get to 25: _____

3.

	A	B	C	D
1	12		=B4/3	
2		=A1*3		
3				=C1*4
4		=B2−12		

To get to 25: _____

4.

	A	B	C	D
1		=B3+3.5		=A2+9
2	5		=B1/5	
3		=D1−2.5		=C2*4
4				

To get to 25: _____

5.

	A	B	C	D
1		15.3	=B1/3	
2				=A4−.5
3				=D2+5
4	=C1+14.7			

To get to 25: _____

6.

	A	B	C	D
1	=(B2+1)*4			
2		=C3/2		=A1/2
3			=D4/2	
4				1

To get to 25: _____

7.

	A	B	C	D
1	=A3−7.9		9.2	
2		=A1/2		
3		=C1*3		=B2*3−.05
4				

To get to 25: _____

8.

	A	B	C	D
1		=B2/26		
2		5.2		
3		=A4−20		=B3+9
4	=C1*2			

To get to 25: _____

Graphing Your Data

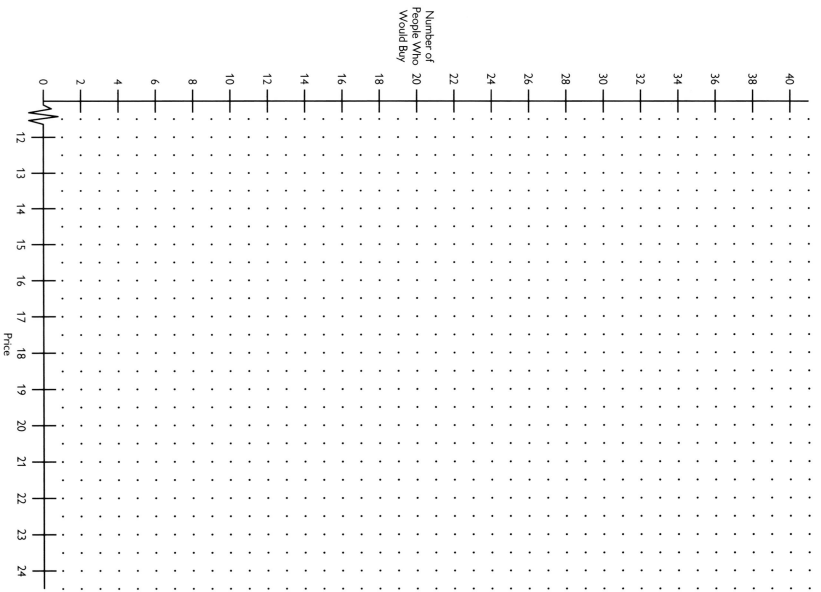

Number of People Who Would Buy

Price

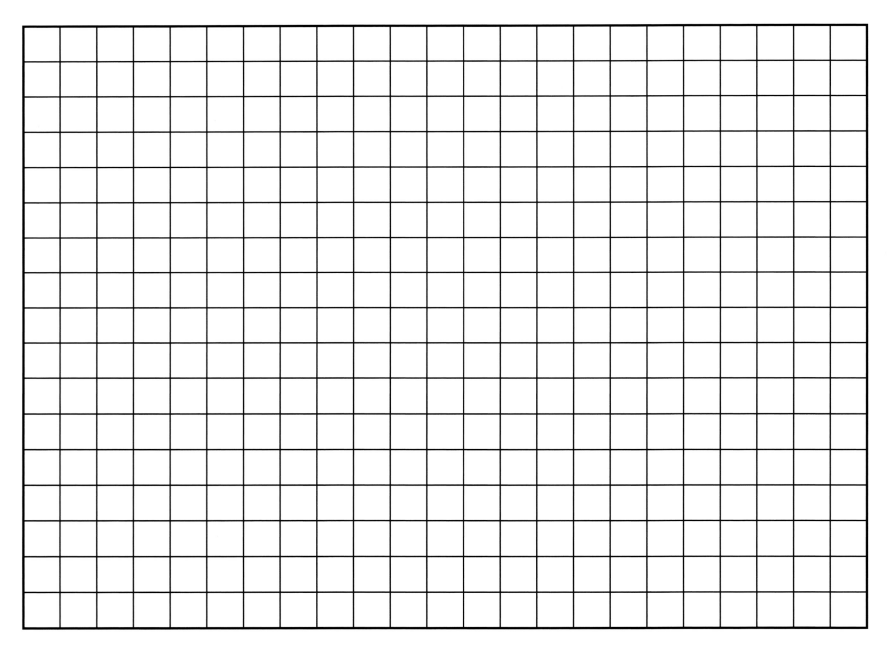

Centimeter Grid Paper

Tee-Time's Profits

Tee-Time is concerned about the overall trends in its profit rather than day-to-day changes. It reports its profit once a month. The first five descriptions below show the profit reported for the months of August–January. Use the graph at the right to figure out which month is being described, and explain why you chose that month. The descriptions are not in order.

1. A rumor is spread that Tee-Time has a new custom-printed T-shirt, so its sales increase a lot. Because of the additional business, Tee-Time hires a few additional part-time employees. This month it has $2,000 more income than the previous month, but its expenses have gone up also by $500.

2. Weekend Wear, Tee-Time's main competitor, has a special sale this month so people go to Weekend Wear more often than Tee-Time. Tee-Time's sales drop off. This month its income has gone down by $500. Its expenses, however, have remained the same.

3. Tee-Time sells more T-shirts than usual. This month it has $1,000 more income than the previous month. However, it had to buy more T-shirts than usual to replace those it sold. So expenses go up by $500.

4. Tee-Time's inventory managers start buying higher quality T-shirts to sell, so Tee-Time's expenses go up $1,000. Its income stays the same.

5. Tee-Time runs out of several good colors of T-shirts this month, so fewer people buy T-shirts. Its income goes down by $1,000. However, one of the clerks quits to go back to college, so expenses also go down by $1,000.

6. Write your own descriptions for the months of February and March.

The next two descriptions explain what happened in April and May. Read the descriptions, and then draw the rest of the graph at the right to match the descriptions.

7. In April, Tee-Time's inventory managers find a cheaper supplier who will sell them high quality T-shirts at a lower cost. Tee-Time's expenses go down $1,000, but its income stays the same.

8. In May, Tee-Time moves to a new, larger store. The costs of moving make expenses go up $2,000 this month. However, in its new location, many new customers come to the store, so income goes up by $1,000.

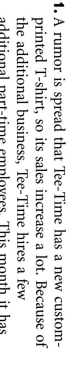

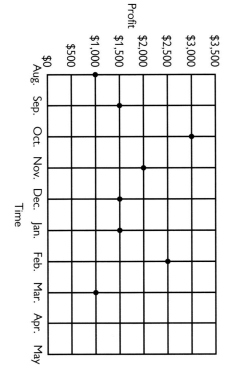

Missing Graphs

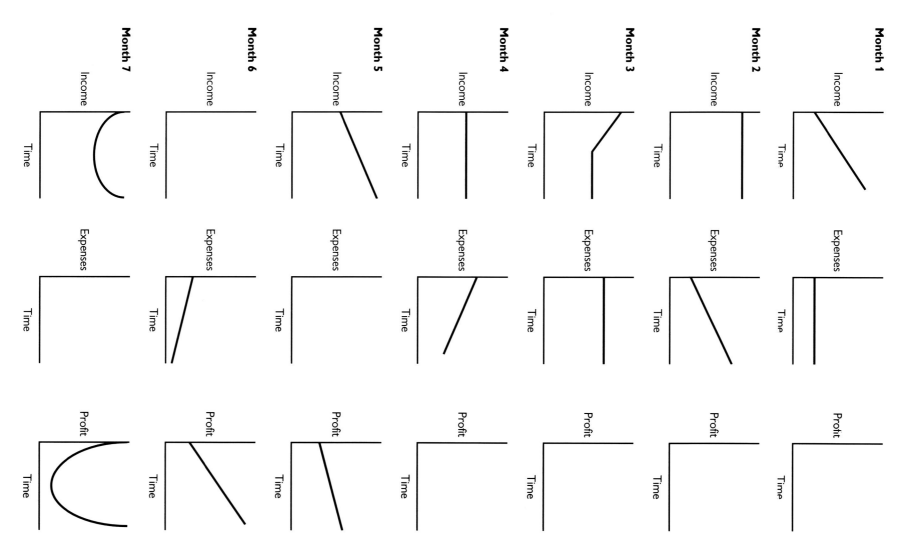

North Mall Cinema

North Mall Cinema Project Sequence

Student Investigation

		Lesson	Date
1.	Organize the data given in Information About North Mall Cinema.	10	_____
2.	List what-if questions to explore.	10	_____
3.	Design a spreadsheet.	11	_____
4.	Investigate profit on the spreadsheet.	11	_____
5.	Create a report on improving profit.	12	_____

Information About North Mall Cinema

Capacity	There are four theaters, each showing a different movie. Each theater can hold 300 people.
Hours	The cinema is open every day from noon to midnight. Each theater shows movies at noon, 3 P.M., 6 P.M., and 9 P.M. each day.
Prices	$6.00 for adults. $4.00 for children 12 and under.
Average Attendance	475 adults per day for each theater. 100 children per day for each theater. During the first two weeks a movie is out, these numbers double.
Employees	Each day there should be 20 full-time employees on duty. They each work 8 hours a day, and make $7.00 an hour. When the accountants figure out the budget, they divide the amount for salaries evenly among the four theaters.
Rental Fees	Each movie costs $1,000 to rent a day. During the first two weeks a movie is out, the rental fee is $2,000 per day.
Building Costs & Utilities	The cinema company pays an average of $1,800 per day for the building costs. This covers rent, heat, electricity, phone, and insurance. When the accountants figure out the budget, they divide the amount for building costs and utilities evenly among the four theaters.

Predicting Profits

PART I

For each what-if question, decide whether income, expenses, and profit would increase, decrease, or stay the same. Draw an upward arrow (↑) to show them increasing, a downward arrow (↓) to show them decreasing, and an equal sign (=) to show them staying the same.

What-If Question	Income	Expenses	Profit
1. What if the cinema had fewer theaters open?			
2. What if the theaters expanded so each could now hold more people?			
3. What if the cinema company hired more employees?			
4. What if the rental fees for each movie went down?			
5. What if the theater decides to show movies more times each day?			
6. Write your own what-if question here.			
7. Write your own what-if question here.			
8. Write your own what-if question here.			

PART II

The graphs below show general trends in profit over a period of time. For the first five what-if questions in Part I, choose a graph that shows what would happen to profit. Describe why you think the graph is the right choice. Hint: You might use a graph more than once, and you might not use some of the graphs at all. Choose from these graphs:

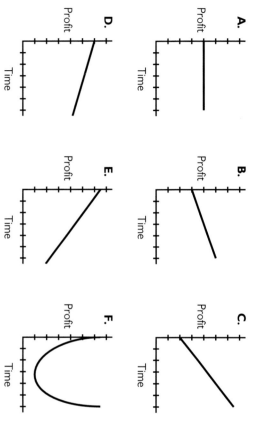

A.

Profit

Time

B.

Profit

Time

C.

Profit

Time

D.

Profit

Time

E.

Profit

Time

F.

Profit

Time

PART III

Describe what would happen to income and expenses for what-if questions 6, 7, and 8 from Part I. For each question, make a graph like the one shown to the right. Show what would happen to profit on each graph.

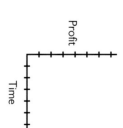

Profit

Time

INDEX

using metric units of length,
FTGU 10, 11, 15–29
perimeter,
FTGU 16, 22, A31
GIS 64–65
polygon angle,
GIS 32, 40–43, A34
precision in,
FTGU 11, 22–25, 29
rate,
BB 10, 11, 14–29, A29–A32
surface area of a polyhedron,
FTGU 44–47
weight estimation,
BB 22

Median
FTGU 64–65

Metric system
area,
FTGU 11, 12, 26–29,
A29–A31
benchmarks for length,
FTGU 22
length,
FTGU 10, 11, 15–29,
A29–A31

Modeling
divisibility,
MMA 54, 58–61, A37
equal ratios,
BB 38
equations,
LOA 55, 66–69, A39
inequalities,
LOA 10, 18–21, A30
integer addition and
subtraction,
MMA 10, 13–21, A29, A30
integer multiplication and
division,
MMA 11, 13, 22–25, A31
linear motion,
LOA 40–41
outcomes,
CE 46, 47, 50–61, A35–A37
percent,
BB 54, 55, 58–59, 62–65,
70–73, A38
probability,
CE 11, 22–25, 27–44, A31,
A32–A34
proportion,
BB 44

Models. *See also* Scale drawing;
Scale model
evaluating,

FTGU 55, 70–73, A40
nets,
FTGU 32, 34, 36–43, 55,
67–69
simulations,
CE 63–80, A38–A40
of three-dimensional figures,
FTGU 32, 34, 36–43, 55,
63–69

Multiple representations
equations, tables, graphs,
LOA 42–43, 55, 70–73,
A34, A40
equations, tables, graphs,
words,
LOA 46–47
equations, tables, ordered
pairs,
LOA 38–39, A33
equations and tables of values,
LOA 17, 29, A29, A32
equivalent expressions,
LOA 11, 22–25, A31
using equivalent integer
operations,
MMA 11, 26–29, A32
of inequalities,
LOA 10, 18–21, A30
integer models and equations,
MMA 10, 11, 18–25, A30,
A31
mathematical and verbal
expressions,
LOA 10, 14–17, A29
nets and three-dimensional
figures,
FTGU 36–43
percent and circle graphs,
BB 54, 62–65, A38
percent, fractions, decimals,
BB 54, 58–61, A37
for pi,
GIS 54, 58–61
probabilities as fractions,
decimals, and percents,
CE 11, 22–25, 28, 29,
36–43, A31, A33, A34
ratios and charts,
BB A33
ratios and graphs,
BB 37
ratios and tables,
BB 39
scale drawing and model,
FTGU 66–69
spreadsheets and graphs,
GDTB 46, 54–57, A36

statements and graphs,
GDTB 47, 58–61, A37
tables and graphs,
BB 10, 18–21, 64–65, A30
GDTB 46, 50–53, A35
visual models and numerical
probabilities,
CE 46, 50–61, A35–A37
words and numbers for
probabilities,
CE 28, 36–39, A33

Multiples
MMA 54, 62–65, A38

Multiplication
algebraic properties and,
LOA 11, 22–25, A31
decimal,
GIS 54, 55, 58–69, A37–A39
factors,
MMA 54, 62–65, A38
of fractions,
MMA 32, 40–43, A34
integer,
MMA 11, 22–25, A31
spreadsheet formulas,
GDTB 36–37

N

NCTM Curriculum Standards
correlation checklist,
All units, see page 5

Negative numbers, in spreadsheets and their graphs,
GDTB 46, 54–57

Nets, for three-dimensional
figures
FTGU 32, 34, 36–43, 55,
63–69

North Mall Cinema project
profit, income, expense,
what-if questions,
GDTB 64, 68–75, A38
profit recommendations,
GDTB 65, 76–79, A40
spreadsheet analysis,
GDTB 64, 72–75, A39

Number line
inequalities on,
LOA 10, 18–21, A30
percents and fractions on,
BB 58–59

Number sense. *See also*
Estimation

checking for reasonable
answers,
BB 18–19
converting data to appropriate
units,
LOA 26–27
graph-slope relationship,
BB 10, 18–21, A30
relating equations and graphs,
LOA 33, 44–47, A35
relating equations and tables
of values,
LOA 17, 29, 39, A29, A32
unit selection,
BB 16–17

Number theory
composite number,
MMA 54, 62–65, A38
divisibility,
MMA 54, 56, 58–61, A37
perfect squares,
MMA 32, 33, 36–39, 48–51,
A33, A36
prime factors,
MMA 54, 62–65, A38
prime numbers,
MMA 54, 62–65, A38

Numeration
exponents,
MMA 32, 33, 36–51,
A33–A36
multiples,
MMA 54, 62–65, A38
roots,
MMA 33, 38–39, 44–47,
A33, A35, A36, A40
signed numbers,
MMA 9–30, A29–A32
square numbers,
MMA 32, 33, 36–39, 48–51,
A33, A36

O

Obtuse angle
GIS 16–17, A29

Obtuse triangle
GIS 11, 22–25, A31

Order
decimal,
FTGU 28, 50
probability,
CE 47, 58–61, A37
on a probability line,
CE 11, 22–25, A31

unit prices,
BB 14–15, 24–25

Order of operations, spreadsheet
formulas and
GDTB 28, 36–39, A33

Ordered pairs, from equations
LOA 38–39, A33

Origin, coordinate plane
LOA 36–37

Outcome grid
CE 46, 47, 50–61, A35–A37

P

Parallel lines
GIS 32, 36–39, A33

Parallelogram
area of,
FTGU 35
properties of,
GIS 32, 36–39, A33

Parents, reporting to
BB, MMA, FTGU, LOA,
GIS A2, A20;
CE, GDTB A2, A24

Patterns
area and cost,
FTGU 4, 58–61
diameter and circumference
of a circle,
GIS 54, 58–61
divisibility,
MMA 54, 58–61, A37
in the equations of horizontal
and vertical lines,
LOA 44–45, A35
exponential,
MMA 48–51
Fibonacci Sequence,
CE 35
lines of symmetry for regular
polygons,
GIS 33, 48–51
on a multiplication chart,
MMA 55, 66–69, A39
in the ordered pairs for an
equation,
LOA 38–39, A33
perfect square,
MMA 32, 36–39, A33
polygon sides and angles,
GIS 32, 40–43, A34
predicting with,
LOA 11, 26–29, 33, 48–51,
55, 70–73, A32, A36, A40

games by probability of
winning,
CE 47, 58–61, A37
probabilities,
CE 11, 22–25, A31

Rate
price graph of,
BB 10, 18–21, A30
total price and,
BB 11, 26–29, A32
unit price,
BB 9–30, A29–A32

Ratio. See also Percent; Rate
BB 32, 36–43, A33, A34
comparison,
BB 32, 36–37, 40–43, A34
cross products and,
BB 42–43, A34
equal,
BB 38–41, A33
pi,
GIS 54, 56–61, A37
probabilities expressed as,
CE 11, 12, 22–25, 28, 29,
36–43, 47, 58–61, A31, A33,
A34, A37
proportion and,
BB 33, 44–51, A35, A36
scale and,
FTGU 18–25, A29–A31
table,
BB 38–39

Ray
GIS 14

Reasonable answers, estimation
and,
FTGU 54, 55, 62–65

Rectangle
area,
FTGU 11, 12, 26–29, A32
area formula,
FTGU 12, 29
circle area and,
GIS 55, 66–69, A39
polygon area and,
GIS 54, 62–65, A38
properties of,
GIS 32, 36–39, A33

Reflex angle
GIS 16–17, A29

Regular polygon
GIS 42–43
area of,
GIS 62–64

Relative numbers. See Percent;
Proportion; Rate; Ratio

Resources
All units, see page 8

Rhombus
properties of,
GIS 32, 36–39, A33

Right angle
GIS 16–17, A29
symbol,
GIS 17

Right triangle
GIS 11, 22–25, A31

Roots
cubic,
MMA 33, 35, 44–47, A35,
A36, A40
square,
MMA 35, 38–39, 46–47,
A33

Rotation
GIS 11, 26–29, A32

Rounding
decimals,
GIS 55, 66–69, A39
to the nearest cent,
BB 10, 11, 14–17, 22–25,
A29, A31
to the nearest percent,
BB 54, 62–65
to the nearest whole number,
BB 54, 62–65
percent estimation and,
BB 60–61

Rubrics
assessment,
BB, MMA, FTGU, LOA, GIS
A2, A6–A7, A10–A11,
A14–A15, A18–A19;
CE, GDTB A2, A6–A7,
A10–A11, A14–A15,
A18–A19, A22–A23

S

Sale price
BB 55, 66–69, A39

Sales
price relationship,
GDTB 46, 50–53, A35

Scale
FTGU 2, 4, 10, 12, 55

proportion and,
FTGU 15–21, 56, A29–A31
ratio and,
FTGU 15–25
size and,
FTGU 10, 15–25, A29, A30

Scale drawing
floor plan,
FTGU 10, 15–17, 67–69,
A29
site plan,
FTGU 10, 18–21, 67–69,
A30
wall plan,
FTGU 26–30, A32

Scale model
roof model,
FTGU 32, 34, 36–43, 55,
67–69, A33, A34
wall model,
FTGU 11, 22–25, 67–69,
A31

Scalene triangle
GIS 11, 22–25, A31

Scatter plot
GDTB 46, 48, 50–53, A35

Sides
classifying polygons by,
GIS 32, 36–39, A33
classifying triangles by,
GIS 10, 11, 18–25, A30, A31

Signed numbers. See also
Integers
MMA 9–30, A29–A32

Simulation software
GDTB 13

Simulations
designing,
CE 64, 65, 72–79, A39, A40
income, expense, profit,
GDTB 10–12, 18–25
likelihood of events in,
CE 68–69
testing,
CE 64, 68–71, 78–79, A38

Site plan
drawing,
FTGU 10, 18–21, A30
guidelines for,
FTGU 19
Skill Check
BB, MMA, FTGU, LOA,
GIS A2, A8, A12, A16;

CE, GDTB A2, A8,
A12, A16, A20

Skill Quiz
BB, MMA, FTGU, LOA,
GIS A8, A12, A16;
CE, GDTB A8, A12,
A16, A20

Slope
relationship to a linear
equation,
LOA 42–43
steepness relationship,
BB 10, 18–21, A30

Spatial reasoning. See also
Modeling
classifying angles,
GIS 10, 14–17, A29
classifying polygons,
GIS 11, 22–25, 32, 36–39,
A31, A33
cost graph,
BB 10, 18–21, A30
estimating angle measure,
GIS 14–17, A29
estimating area,
GIS 55, 66–69, A39
graphs of spreadsheet data,
GDTB 46, 54–57, A36
integer operations with cubes,
MMA 13, 14–25, A29–A31
making a rectangle from a
circle,
GIS 55, 66–69
making a rectangle from a
polygon,
GIS 54, 62–65
outcomes on a grid,
CE 46, 47, 50–61, A35–A37
percent as a circle graph,
BB 54, 62–65, A38
probability on area models,
CE 27–44, A32–A34
probability on a line,
CE 11, 22–25, 64, 72–75,
A31, A38
qualitative graphs,
GDTB 47, 58–61, A37
scale drawing,
FTGU 10, 15–21, 67–69,
A33, A34
scale model,
FTGU 22–25, 36–43,
67–69, A31, A33, A34
symmetry,
GIS 24–25, 33, 48–51, A31,

A36
tessellations,
GIS 11, 26–29, 33, 44–47,
A32, A35
two-dimensional nets for
three-dimensional figures,
FTGU 32, 34, 36, 43, 52
walking on the coordinate
plane,
LOA 32, 40–41

Spreadsheet software
business analysis,
GDTB 13
common mistakes,
GDTB 49
for cost estimation,
FTGU 57
entering information,
GDTB 30
graphing options,
BB 57
graphs and,
GDTB 49
long-term savings
calculations,
BB 13
spreadsheet presentation,
GDTB 66
spreadsheet setup,
LOA 13
tables of values and,
LOA 13
for testing equivalent
expressions,
LOA 13

Spreadsheets
GDTB 27–44, A32–A34
design,
GDTB 64, 72–75
entering data on,
GDTB 28, 32–35, A32
formulas,
GDTB 28, 29, 36–44, A33,
A34
graphing from,
GDTB 46, 54–57, A36
order of operations and,
GDTB 28, 36–39, A33
steps for planning,
GDTB 40–41
what-if questions and,
GDTB 28, 29, 32–35,
40–43, 64, 68–75

Square
properties of,

MATHSCAPE
ACRONYMS
AND
UNIT TITLES

BB
Buyer Beware

CE
Chance Encounters

FTGU
From the Ground Up

GDTB
Getting Down to
Business

GIS
Getting In Shape

LOA
The Language of
Algebra

MMA
Making Mathematical
Arguments